LA FAMI

Angela Lily Cole

Edited by Heidi Lindsay

Table of Contents

Dedication

To my mother, Erietta, and father, Noti, I thank you for a lifetime of beautiful memories and a wonderful childhood growing up. Without you both, I wouldn't be the person I am today. This book truly encapsulates their life stories, both the beautiful times and the tragedies they faced.

To my beloved Frankie, my husband, soul mate and best friend, I thank you for our wonderful life together and the many adventures and laughs we shared. Always loved and remembered.

Acknowledgements

This book is very special as it brings to life the many stories I was told growing up. With special thanks to Maria, my wonderful daughter, and Heidi, my lovely granddaughter, who helped transform my decades of notes and memories into this final masterpiece.

A special thanks also to Margarita Petropoulou, Mitzi Berglund-Meletis and Kornilios Selamsis for helping piece together the final segments of the family's history and the family tree. During this incredible journey, we have now discovered new things we never knew of those long ago, as well as connecting with family members who were before just names on paper.

With love also to our boys, Richard, Robert and Michael, and all our grandchildren, Rebecca, Heidi, Tom, Ethan and Gemma. I would like to make a special mention to the latest addition to the family, our great-granddaughter, Little Faith, who brings so much joy to my life with her boundless energy and her infectious giggle. You have made my life complete. I am truly blessed to have you all in my life and I wish you all the courage to follow your dreams, just like I have. Indeed, you are not old until your dreams become regrets and the rainbow ceases to exist. I am convinced that the difficult times happen to make a story.

Me with my great-granddaughter, Faith.

About the Author

From a very young age, I have always been intrigued by my parents' and grandparents' stories. I have always cherished the shared memories and the stories of people who were significant in their lives. Growing up, I was mesmerised by these stories and started to write them down. Years and years of storytelling and note-taking has led me to present you with the tale of Erietta and Noti—my mother and father. Sadly, if these stories were not written down or narrated to others, they would simply be washed away like a grain of sand taken away by a wave. Whilst holding old, worn photographs of loved ones, our future generations would have been clueless as to who those people were and what stories they had to tell. Now, I am confident that my children, grandchildren, and great-grandchildren will know of the stories of all the people who were significant in my life. I smile at the thought of these stories continuing to live on as a legacy.

Writing these stories and reliving them through my family and the birth of this book has kept my memories and stories alive—a fire never to be put out. I am proud that my heritage and ancestry will be carried through future generations and that this story is evidence of the love and memories that have run through the family.

Before I begin this book, I wanted to share my own life story through photographs and memories, so you can picture the wonderful life I have had growing up.

I was born in a beautiful place called Heliopolis, the City of the Sun, on 23rd July 1932. Being one of the oldest cities in ancient Egypt, Heliopolis brought majestic beauty with its history. Despite many beautiful memories, little remains of the great city today. The sole surviving monument is the Obelisk of Sesostris I, known as Cleopatra's Needle. It now proudly stands in the Thames Embankment in London and in Central Park in New York City. Obelisks were originally erected in pairs at the entrances of ancient Egyptian temples, with the shafts embellished with hieroglyphs. The history of ancient Egypt is phenomenal and is an important part of my heritage—it is the place where my mother and father met.

Being the firstborn, I was the apple of my mother and father's eye. They had always wanted children.

Me as a toddler. Me and my mum in Alexandria.

When I was five, my mum and dad had twin girls— Maria (Mitzi) and Fanoula (Fani). Secretly, my dad always wanted a boy to carry on the family name, so when the girls arrived on 2nd April 1938, my dad thought it was an April Fools' Joke. There were no baby scans in those days, so it was a huge surprise that my mum had given birth to twins— and girls.

I was named after my great grandmother Anghela— carrying on the family name was a tradition in our family.

Maria was named after her stepmother and Fanoula after her grandmother, who you will read about in the book. You will also come to understand why the name Fani was no longer passed on throughout the generations.

The three sisters—me in the middle with my twin sisters, Maria (left) and Fanoula (right).

Growing up, I had a beautiful life and was brought up in a loving home, where learning languages was welcomed. I studied Arabic as a child as we lived in an Arab country. I quickly found I had an aptitude for learning, and learning languages became my favourite pastime. In fact, studying became my passion and my mantra. I got my love for learning languages from my mother, who was fluent in

Arabic, English, Greek, Italian, French and German. I followed in my mother's footsteps, apart from German.

Here I am in my school uniform in a French school I attended. However, I was quickly taken out of that school for learning swear words.

In my teenage years, I attended the English Mission College, which helped me to boost my language skills which enabled me to attend university. The college was beautiful, and it had a swimming pool in the gardens. It was an added bonus if you attended a school with a pool as Egypt is a very hot country.

The swimming pool at the English Mission College in Cairo where I learned all my languages.

I became the first person in the family to go to university. Getting enrolled in the prestigious American University in Cairo to study modern languages meant I had three years of undisputable hard work in front of me to get a degree in my hands. Living in Egypt meant I had to have at least a smattering of Arabic too, so my father, Noti, arranged an Arabic teacher for private tuition at home. I remember rather clearly that in desperation, he used to grasp his hair and, in a voice that made me jump, would say, "You are gifted in all the other languages. Why can you not grasp Arabic? Enti Homâra!" (You are a donkey). I was hopeless at Arabic, especially when it came to writing it. The teacher simply could not understand why I couldn't comprehend this particular language.

My mother, Erietta, would categorically forbid me from staying up later than midnight to study, saying that I needed my sleep to keep up with my studies. So, surreptitiously when I knew she was asleep, like a thief in the night, I would take my books and notepad and go into our colossal bathroom with its cool marble floor and study, until one day she caught me. She knocked on the door quietly and said the dreaded words: "Open up immediately, or I'll call your father!" Looking around in panic, I saw the large bath containing all the white clothes that were steeping overnight to be ready for the washerwoman coming the next morning to wash and hang out. Feeling like Marie Antoinette when she was taken to the guillotine, I quickly put my notepad and red book underneath the washing, silently steeping in the bath.

After opening the door and insisting that I was simply on the toilet, my mother searched high and low for evidence to suggest otherwise. When she found nothing, she excused me. I had got away with it. And with a look of triumph, I swept past my mum to go to bed. The next morning, there was pandemonium in the household. All the washing that was in the bath had turned a very red hue. I leave it to your imagination as to what happened next.

My dad and I travelled together, visiting some spectacular places. We went to Paris, Capri in Italy and visited the Catacombs in Rome. He expressed the importance of visiting these places, saying, "If we don't visit them, you may never see them again." And he was right.

Me and my dad on the beach during our travels.

Me and my dad in Rome, Italy with the Saint Michael the Archangel statue behind us.

We had neighbours, Mr and Mrs Mansourian, who lived on the first floor. Mr Mansourian was an ambassador. I was invited to attend the Embassy in Cairo, to celebrate the arrival of a new ambassador, and this was to welcome him. I was dressed in a beautiful long dress and veil and had my photograph taken. I felt like a celebrity. A beautiful banquet was laid, and all the ladies were dressed in their fineries.

Elegantly dressed in my long gown and veil ready for the Embassy invitation ceremony.

Whilst at university, myself and three of my friends dared each other to attempt to climb the Great Pyramid of Giza, the oldest of the Seven Wonders of the Ancient World and the only one that is still standing. To put into context how big it was, the pyramid itself is 481 feet high, comprising 2.3 million stones, with a total mass of 6.5 million tons. My friends and I defied the odds and fearlessly climbed one-third of the way up the pyramid—at midnight. I used to be a bit of a dare-devil back in the day.

Me and my friends at the Pyramids of Giza in Egypt, which we climbed one-third of the way.

Me riding on a camel in Cairo—it wasn't easy riding a camel.

After leaving university with top marks, I was headhunted and landed my first job interview at Coca Cola. I became one of three secretaries. My then-husband, Alberto, worked as an accountant clerk for the company.

Outside the Coca Cola
company entrance with Huda,
one of the girls I worked with.

Me posing as Miss Coca Cola
for a company promotion.

Rumour had it that Cecil B. DeMille had built a great city out in the desert, and they were hiring film extras, at a triple of what we earned in our jobs. So, Alberto and I took two weeks of vacation and enrolled. The film was called The Ten Commandments with the actor, Charlton Heston, in the cast. DeMille had hired at least 14,000 extras and 15,000 animals. It was one of the most epic films ever produced and the most expensive production. It was a thrilling experience indeed.

With the Suez Crisis, I had to flee from Egypt to England in 1957. At the time, I had recently given birth to my first child, Richard. Alberto and I were separated, with him being forced to flee the country by boat with his mother, Nona. When Richard was three months old, we boarded a flight with Trans World Airlines to take me to England. On the first stop in Zürich, Switzerland, the captain radioed the Red Cross to inform them that there was a mother and baby on board. When we landed, they took Richard and gave him a bottle and a little wash, while I enjoyed a hot drink and a sandwich. Now refreshed, we made our way to Greece, where we stayed with Aunty Danae, Uncle Damy and Marietta so they could meet the baby. Our final stop was London where Alberto was waiting for us. I was reunited with my husband, and we set up home in Brecknock Road, Kent.

At the airport with baby Richard in my arms, accompanied by the pilot of Trans World Airlines, Mitzi and a few others before we boarded the plane.

Alberto and I later had two more children, Robert, and Maria, and we had some happy family memories. Watching the children grow up was so precious.

Family photo—Me, Alberto and our three children, Maria, Richard and Robert in Kent.

Me and the three children.

I became a teacher of French at the prestigious Northfleet School for Girls in Meopham, Kent, for two years. There was only one problem—I couldn't drive, and being in the sticks there were only a few buses running. This meant I would turn up late for registration. So, I bought a second-hand car and hired a driving instructor. Hugette who was my assistant at the time gave me lessons too. My pupils had a field day with my 'L' plates. My Head of Languages used to laughingly say, "On the day of your driving test, be sure to wear a dress with a "low décollete". I don't know whether it was a fluke but after my fifth attempt, I passed. Hip hip hooray! Driving is something I have always disliked, and if I was to drive now, I would probably be banned.

Me with my assistant Hugette outside Biddenden Road, Kent with my blue car—a Standard 10.

After Kent, I moved to Sunderland as there were more job opportunities. I taught French, Italian and Greek at Southmoor School for quite a few years. I also used to do private evening Greek lessons, where I had many pupils. This is where I met my soul mate Frank. When I met Frank, I didn't know him from Adam; he was my pupil. He won a competition from a friend, Smithy, who owned a garage. He asked if I would like to go with him. So I did, and the rest is history. We became ignited.

From 1971 to 1983, I merged my family life with my work as a multi-lingual supervisor and secretary for Coles Cranes, an engineering company in Sunderland. I loved my job and going to work was a pleasure.

Me working at Coles Cranes as a supervisor of the typing pool, along with two of my assistants.

When Coles Cranes went into liquidation, I took stock of my life, refusing to remain a jobless statistic. With my gift of tongues, a secretarial background, and my assets, including a telephone, a portable typewriter, and the use of a family car, I made the decision to become self-employed. I had to get it right!

I wanted work that combined my love of languages with my secretarial skills, and while working at Coles Cranes, I had done some freelance work part-time for the police as an interpreter. With this experience and my £1,000 redundancy money, I decided to set up an interpreting and translating service. In 1981, Norman Tebbit, a politician, quoted that the unemployed should "get on your bike and look for work". After reading an article in the local newspaper, I attended a seminar and found I had a lot to learn if I was to turn my idea into a reality. I was interviewed and accepted onto a free two days a week 'Skills into Business' course at the Sunderland Polytechnic, starting in April 1983 for eight weeks. I emerged with new knowledge and confidence.

After the course, I applied for the New Enterprise Allowance, which was a £40-a-week grant for the first year of business. I set up my business in the living room and used the Post Office's business help scheme to make a start. This comprised of sending out 1000 free first-class letters for the business, to which I sourced the addresses of 1000 firms and organisations likely to need my services.

Shortly afterwards, and with Tebbit's advice, I got on my bike and started looking for work. Thus, Angela Walker Interpreting & Translating Services was born. I was always fuelled by determination and focus, and this led me to become a successful businesswoman. I loved the feeling of being the boss.

Angela is set up by Tebbit's advice

A WOMAN who was made redundant has set up her own interpreting and translation business — thanks to the Industry Secretary's advice.

Mrs Angela Walker decided to go it alone after becoming redundant at a large engineering company lat last year.

I featured in numerous local press articles about my initiative and venture from unemployment to self-employment. I became a freelance interpreter for Northumbria Police on a 24-hour call basis, often going to Durham and Newcastle Courts to represent people who didn't speak English. If there was a friendly football match, my language skills were used for fans who were unruly and had to be put into temporary custody until the end of the game. The police at the match told me that the custody cell was pink so that the men who were in would feel silly, hence having a calming effect. Working too for the Home Office, I had to sign the Official Secrets Act. Here I am featured in one of many articles about my journey as an entrepreneur, along with some words of wisdom.

Now it isn't all Greek to Angela

ANGELA .... :
translating

"I was ten hours on the shop-floor once, interpreting for an Italian engineer who was teaching local staff how to use a new machine," she says proudly. Her technical knowledge means that she can offer the right mix for the North-East. Interpreting here means scientific, technical, commercial — not poetry or novels.

Now she has started a Greek class at Monkwearmouth College — for Greek-ans who want to learn some of the language for their holidays.

Mother of four grown-up children, Angela feels that taking the plunge into self-employment was an excellent move for her.

"Every day is a thrill of expectancy — what's in the post, who rings up with an assignment. And working from home is definitely easier than going out to work," she says.

Have you an idea you could turn into a one-woman freelance business? Could be secretarial, languages, freelance housekeeping, even cooking or driving. You'd be surprised how many firms or individuals would "buy in" something like typing, or domestic help from time to time — enough to keep you in business *provided* your work is excellent, not average and you really do enjoy it.

Here are some tips based on Angela's experience . . .
DO start by going to one of the M.S.C. business courses. They run most of the time, are free and will give you a network of friends and contacts as well as invaluable business know-how. Contact Frank Patterson at Sunderland Poly for details.
DO put in for the Enterprise Allowance. The £40 a week grant has been given to all sorts of businesses ranging from freelance writers to klassograms. You need £1,000 but you can get a loan if you don't have the actual cash. Contact Muriel Hindmarsh at Entrust in Sunderland.
DO buy or rent an answering machine if you're offering any sort of service. Most people dislike them — but they do give your business more authenticity if you'll be out a lot.
DO get two of anything that's fundamental to your business. For example, two

irons if you planned a small laundering service (I know of three which have started up from women's homes and they're all doing well) — two typewriters if it's secretarial. You can't afford to lose time and money if something breaks down. Mobile hairdressers have known this for years — they always carry two hairdryers!
DON'T expect immediate results from publicity. Mailshots and adverts won't bring in a flood of replies . . . . now. But someone may keep your letter or ad for six months and look you up when they need you. Don't rely on even that, of course . . . you need to keep marketing all the time.
DON'T get depressed when you have a slow week. It doesn't mean your business is folding . . . it means it's a slow week. Use the time to chase up letters, plot out some new ideas, catch up on chores — even go swimming or walking! It's *your* business and you can do what you like with your time.

BE PREPARED to work extremely hard when you're needed. Clients won't take kindly to excuses about how you can't work late or at weekends.

In our series we've covered every area of the help available in the area to ease women into work. There are schemes courses, programmes and business advice centres in bewildering numbers . . . you should be able to find one!
Good luck.

WHAT LANGUAGE BARRIER?

If it's all Greek to you, the chances are it's all perfectly understandable to ANGELA BONNICI. Why? because she speaks fluent Greek and French and Italian and Arabic and Spanish and English!

Relieving as it may be to know that the Supervisor of our typing pool can speak English, Angela could not be blamed if she had never learned our language. Born of Greek parents in Egypt, the early part of Angela's life was completely foreign to the British lifestyle. "The women of Egyptian households did no housework" she told Coles News. "We were doomed to the tiresome existence of being waited on by a troop of servants! When I came to Britain 19 years ago, I couldn't even boil an egg — I can now though!"

Since she joined Coles four years ago, Angela's skill with languages has been put to frequent good use in the course of the job. In a multinational company like Coles, telexes, invoices and masses of other documentation pour in from every corner of the world in many languages. "Some of the middle-eastern customers insist that we correspond with them in their own language," Angela explained. "It saves time occasionally when arranging credit and shipping details if I send a reply in Arabic by return of telex."

Not surprisingly, Angela's fluency with six languages is also well known outside the Company. Earlier this month, she used part of a free day to help out with interpretation in the Immigration Office at South Shields. It's not unusual either to find Angela helping the police with their enquiries! Fortunately she is on the right side of the law. "Criminals don't always speak English," she explained. "I once had to take a statement in Spanish from a pick-pocket."

"My languages are my hobby," said Angela "so I quite enjoy helping the police on occasions. I did take exception recently, however to a visit from two uniformed policemen at my house. Plain clothes visits I don't mind but not uniforms. After all, what would the neighbours think?"

CHRISTINE BITTLESTONE (left) and ELLA WALLS (right) ask typing pool supervisor ANGELA BONNICI for some translation assistance with some 'foreign correspondence'.

One night, the police took me to a hospital in South Shields, as a French man had been in a road accident and had severe head injuries. He was shouting and swearing, but nobody could understand him. He was in pain, but what he needed was a bottle to wee in—that's all. He just needed to go. A bottle was given to him and Ipso Facto, the curtains were pulled around him, and the relief all around was great.

Being an Interpreter meant my services were required by other companies, one of which was the car manufacturer, Nissan. Frank would wait outside for me whilst I was working there, and once complained that 10 hours was too much time to be waiting. He often brought me cakes and treats to keep me going.

Working at Nissan as an Interpreter.

Frank and I went travelling around Greece for six weeks, visiting many islands, with just a small backpack carrying essentials. What an experience and the memories that came with it! We visited Santorini, Spinalonga, Mykonos, Paleokastritsa and Tinos, to name a few. Tinos is a small holy island, where, once a year, they bring all the people who need help, lay them on the floor and pray all night, hoping for miracles. Tinos is often called 'The Lourdes of Greece' and has around 700 churches on the island. Spinalonga was one of the most memorable places we visited and one that will always stick in my mind. Despite being a leper colony, the people of Spinalonga had hope and made the best of their lives. The island even had hairdressers, cafes and cinemas, airing concerts by musically-talented islanders, thanks to the Brotherhood of the Sick of Spinalonga, who improved the colony. The Brotherhood were a society of businessmen who were dedicated to improving conditions on the island to enable the people to have a better quality of life. The only condition that the Brotherhood made was a ban of mirrors; nobody wanted to see the effect the disease imposed on the faces of those affected. People didn't go there to simply die.

Here are some photos of Frank and I in Greece. We regularly visited our favourite country.

Frank and I on one of our many holidays in Greece.

Frank gave me the fire in my belly and the zest for life. We used to do Greek dancing together; he was very funny at it. Frank and I, along with my daughter Maria, were featured in the paper for holding a Greek night to fundraise for the Macmillan Nurses. The event involved a demonstration of Geordie Greek dancing. Greek dancing was a love of ours.

All of us Greek dancing and collecting money for the Macmillan nurses.

Frank and I shared our love for Greek dancing.

Frank proposed to me in Holland after a tour of the castle. Being an avid artist, he loved looking at all the old-fashioned paintings. As you can see, we were so happy that day and as it was a spontaneous proposal, he promised me a ring once we got home.

Frank and I after he proposed to me outside a castle in Holland.

Frank and I married in October 1989 on a lovely, sunny day. It was a small gathering of family and friends at the local Civic Centre, but what a day it was! My beloved Frank had decorated the hallway with beautiful fresh flowers, and the day was full of love and laughter. We did not need a big do to declare our love to one another. Frank's best friends,

Ian Smith (Smithy) and his wife, Shirley, were our witnesses.

Frank and I on our wedding day.

Happily married with our witnesses, Ian and Shirley.

Frank and I had many more adventures in life, and we were both successful in our careers. Frank was a successful estate agent in Frederick Street, Sunderland. We spent a lot of time in Greece and had many family holidays in Roda, Corfu. During one holiday, we were even invited to feature on Radio Corfu. I spoke about my life in England and the difference between England and Greece. The Greeks are very nebby and asked what I earned per hour in my job. Frank was miffed that they didn't speak to him.

Being interviewed on Radio Corfu, Greece about my working life in England.

My mother, Erietta, was in a beautiful residential home in her later years of life in Greece, and Frank and I often visited her. The name Erietta lives on in her granddaughter Maria, and her great-granddaughter Heidi, who carry the name Henrietta as their middle names, a strong family tradition for the Greeks.

Frank and I visiting my mother in her home in Greece in 1991.

Shortly after my mother's death in 1992, Frank and I went to Greece to visit her and pay our respects. The photo you see shows Frank telling me to be strong, and although my mother had passed away, I would always have my memories of her. Frank was my protector, my rock and always by my side.

Frank giving me support and well-wishes after my mother passed away.

As you can see, my life has been filled with memories, success and most importantly, love and laughter.

I have led a beautiful life and have three wonderful children. I am not only a grandmother now but also a great-grandmother. At the age of 89, I can now say I have written and published my own book, and what an experience that has been! The words and stories my mother and grandmother spoke about are now encapsulated in this book and brought to life in these very pages. I am indeed very grateful and lucky to God.

In the land of hope, there is no winter.

"I am the **family** face

Flesh perishes, I **live** on,

Projecting trait and **trace**

From **time** to time anon

And leaping from **place** to place

Bringing to light those long buried in the **past**"

-Thomas Harding

Living the Greek dream.

The Descendants of Anthimos Petropoulos

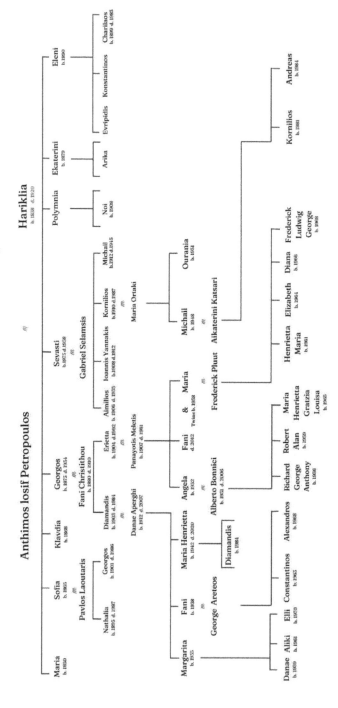

38

Prologue

The time has come to listen to what my beloved Frank used to say, "Hit the deck, Agapi Mou (my love), for we are nothing but a blip across the screen of life—a flash before we vanish."

I am formulating the thread that runs through all the families in the past interlaced with the future for those generations to come. I am proud that the family legacy will be carried out through my children, grandchildren and great-children.

Thus, after many years of listening to and gathering so many tales from my parents and grandparents, I am presenting my family a picture of stories of our ancestry, our *famiglia*.

There have been so many bridges crossed during our lifetime, by so many family members. Alberto and I fleeing Egypt to England during the Suez Crisis. Noti, my beloved father fleeing Smyrna during the holocaust, with Alexandros, his father, and Anghela, his mother. During this time, thousands of Greeks and Armenians were massacred-as told by Edward Hale Bierstadt in the book "The Great Betrayal", which attests and affirms the stories my grandmother Angela, who is featured in the book, used to tell me.

During the summer holidays, my mother and I would stay with my grandmother, who would spend hours telling me her life stories and memories that will unfold throughout these pages. Like a lion waiting patiently in the jungle for its next prey, I would wait until she had her siesta, hungry to know more about the family tales, but a cup of Greek coffee was always needed before the storytelling began. These encapsulating and adventurous tales gave me the hunger to write my book, *La Famiglia,* meaning The Family. My grandmother always used to say, "Once the memories are gone, they are gone," and for that, she was right. The family legacy now lives on for your eyes to read. I hope you love and enjoy the book as much as I have writing it.

Erietta

The Petropoulos Family—A Journey Through Time

The year is 1838

In 1838, three main events took place and were recorded for prosperity:

1. In the USA, the American David Bruce built the first automatic device-printing characters.
2. Andries Pretorius emerged as a new leader in South Africa. He raised a five hundred-men commando team and stopped ten thousand Zulus at the Blood River, killing three thousand.
3. On 26th June, Ranjit Singh signed the Tripartite Treaty. He had done more for the Sikh nation than any ruler had for two hundred years. Uniting the Sikhs, he had created a French-trained army and extended the Sikh power to the borders of British India and Afghanistan.

Lastly, and what was little known and certainly never recorded in any books, was the birth of Hariklia.

Little or nothing was heard about that Greek lady. She had done nothing, achieved little to be given even a small mention anywhere.

One hundred and fifty years later, in 1992, her great-granddaughter Maria, born Meletis, and my sister, accompanied her Swedish husband, Ingemar, to Turkey. He was under a one year's contract to fly through Sultan Airways, a Turkish airline.

Mitzi and her husband, Ingemar.

Finding herself in the exact birthplace as that of her parents and grandparents before her, Maria thought this too good an opportunity to miss—the challenge of tracing her roots. Day after day, she set out looking through dusty Greek Orthodox archives, seeking a name, a family connection amidst the old and moss-grown tombstones.

And there at last—a ghostly family name emerged through the veil of time, that of Hariklia Petropoulos and Anthimos Iosif Petropoulos, her husband.

Hariklia was born in 1838 in Fanari, Constantinople (Istanbul), Turkey. There were no pictures, no stories to be told. Nothing at the time was known about her, but to her surviving great-grandchildren, it was a treasure trove. A piece of their life history, for they now had a written testimony. It wasn't until years later, after further research, that a single photograph of Hariklia was discovered, alongside several photographs of her children.

Returning home, Maria sought out as many aged family members still alive and living in Greece. They then proceeded to remember stories their parents had told them about Hariklia, all those many years ago. Of Anthimos Iosif Petropoulos, not much was known or remembered.

The excitement on the discovery, albeit only two names, two dates of birth and death, could not have been greater than the thrill that Howard Carter felt when he discovered the tomb of Tutankhamen, the Pharaoh, in 1922. No more, no less!

They had each, in their own way, pushed the boundaries of yesteryear further back.

Hariklia and Anthimos went on to have fourteen children—one must remember there were no contraceptives around at this time.

Alas, six of them died. Hardly surprising as the death toll of babies in those far-gone days was abysmal. Their surviving children, one boy and seven girls, were named Georgos, Maria, Sofia, Klavdia, Sevasti, Polymnia, Ekaterini and Eleni.

One hundred and fifty years later, cholera, tuberculosis and jaundice were rife, to name a few of the many endemic diseases. Sanitation and hygiene were not matters that had been perfected to anywhere near today's standards. People, in general, lived to an average age of fifty.

There were no X-rays or heart and lung transplants. Surgery carried out on the foetus whilst still in the mother's womb or the skill of microsurgery in the sewing back of arms and legs, fingers and toes, the implanting back of a woman's egg which had previously been fertilised outside in laboratory conditions, never existed.

Man's walk on the moon, the modern aeroplane and all the numerous achievements of this century, Hariklia and Anthimos' great-grandchildren and their grandchildren now take for granted.

Those things that would have seemed far-fetched, science fiction, albeit even blasphemous, a devil's toy thing, no doubt to all of them, were now not only a reality but unsurprising common knowledge.

Thus, despite all the hardships endured then and certainly despite the lack of surgery and doctors' skills, eight children of Hariklia and Anthimos survived and have thus become the first known direct line of the Petropoulos family roots.

Five of Hariklia's children.

From left to right: Sevasti, Eleni, Sofia, Ekaterini and Polymnia.

Anthimos had his own thriving lumber trading business and had many lumbermen working for him. Being next to a river, the logs were floated to the sawmills, and it was the job of the nimble-footed log drivers to see that the logs did not jam on the way. If they did, they were on hand with long poles to push the logs away.

Life was hard, but the money enabled the Petropoulos family and their children to lead a remarkably comfortable life.

One day, as Anthimos was travelling with some money in gold coins tucked away safely in a pouch inside his clothes, he was waylaid by some Turks who, not being content at merely stealing his money, beat him up mercilessly and left him dying on the wayside.

Word quickly got around that Anthimos was lying dead, and so his friends silently and sadly gathered his beaten body and brought it to Hariklia.

Silently, she cleansed him, anointed him with oils for his final journey and laid him to rest with the blessing of the priests and church in the Greek Orthodox tradition.

This should have been the end of the lumber business— the master had just died, but events were to prove otherwise. Having grieved and cried over the loss of her husband, Hariklia took over the management of the business herself and became the chief breadwinner, and to all accounts made a great success of it all.

This grand lady was indeed a woman of 'tomorrow's world', for she portrayed great strength of character and determination to enter what in her time was strictly a man's world!

Hariklia in Constantinople in 1908.

Hariklia later died at the unbelievable age of eighty-two—her longevity is indeed another source of admiration. To have lived so long in a time where medical science was just a haphazard puzzle just beginning to make sense.

She died in 1920 and is buried in Feriköy, Constantinople, opposite the Catholic Cemetery.

Klavdia (left) and Eleni (right), who sent this photograph to their brother, Georgos. It was signed, *December 12 for Mr. Georgos Petropoulos. Memory of sisterly love and devotion. Your sisters, Klavdia and Eleni.*

Ekaterini and her husband as newlyweds.

Ekaterini graduating from school in Constantinople.

Georgos Petropoulos

Erietta Petropoulos

Erietta Petropoulos was born on 20th June 1904 and was the daughter of Georgos Petropoulous, a prosperous architect. Her brother, Damy, was born on 8th March 1903 in Sidi Gaber, Alexandria, Egypt. Damy was also following in his father's footsteps and was studying in Graz, Austria, to be an architect.

Erietta was a combination of characteristics—tenacious and determined, outspoken to the point of blunt, and yet, surprisingly gentle, kind and ever ready to give her all for those in need of comfort or help. She was a friend to many who valued her honest and outspoken opinions and cared for and treated the household servants with respect, never shouting or imposing impossible tasks, as was the custom around her.

Erietta holding her first-born Angela in a park in Heliopolis, Egypt.

In her figure, as well as her temperament, she favoured her father's side of the family.

Bright and intelligent, she fluently spoke six languages: Greek, French, Italian, Arabic, English and German.

Born to wealth, Erietta had attended the 'in set' school of Notre Dame de Sion as a border. The school's main objective was to churn out the girls with the required and useful knowledge of etiquette, piano playing, proficiency in many languages and good communicating skills—all sought after in the 'step up the ladder' of the marriage stakes.

And yet, a tremendous emphasis was placed on high academic achievement, although none of the girls who attended Notre Dame de Sion would ever need to go in search of a 'paid job'. Nevertheless, they all emerged with a wealth of learning.

Molière, Chaucer, Victor Hugo, Dante, and thinkers such as Sartre and Kafka went hand in hand with algebra, mathematics and embroidery. It meant that the boarders were force-fed a diet of learning to justify the high fees that the school extorted from the parents.

Thus, a picture of a well-to-do girl born to wealth emerges. Soon, Erietta was to fall totally and passionately in love. Whilst on a three-month stay on the island of Chios, Greece, where she had gone with Maria, her stepmother and

Maria's two sisters once more to recuperate with another spell of Maria's depression, Erietta was to meet her first serious love.

He was a lawyer with an already established practice in Piraeus. He was on a two-year leave of absence doing his military service. At present, he was taking a ten-day break from manoeuvres and rigorous training at camp.

They met in a quiet taverna, the local coffee shop, when a friend introduced them. Being about twenty years older, he was understandably quite adept at charming this twenty-two-year-old who was not worldly-wise as far as men were concerned.

It was inevitable that they fell in love. He was smitten by her charm, wit, and sunny disposition and by the fact that Erietta had led a very sheltered life. He proceeded to make a few discreet enquiries around the island, and as the Greeks are notorious at getting to know everyone's business, it soon became apparent that Erietta came from excellent family background.

Upon their return to Alexandria, he continued wooing the girl he so dearly loved now. They met at friends' houses and exchanged many secret love letters.

Outside the ornamental front gates of the Sidi Gaber home in Alexandria, large ornate clay urns were filled with geraniums. It was amongst the blooming flowers that letters were left and collected. Thus, the romance blossomed.

The time had come for the young man now to officially ask Erietta's hand in marriage. Maria, who had no desire to let go of Erietta, who saw her through all her troubled days and from whom she had learned to lean on, understandably did everything in her power to come between the young lovers and put an end to the romance.

She persuaded her husband, Georgos that the young man was not only unsuitable given the twenty or so years difference in age but that it was her duty to inform that she thought the young man was only after Erietta's dowry.

Georgos regretfully agreed with Maria. Although he could see that Erietta was very happy and deeply in love. He had once given his promise to Maria that she would handle the children as she saw fit, but in all truth, had he not done so, it would condemn the whole household to one of Maria's depressive moods and withdrawals—he had no choice!

So, Erietta was forbidden to communicate with her beloved—he was told he was utterly unsuitable. Without any reason given, Erietta was sent to Crete with Maria to get over her infatuation, believing that the man would lose all hope and depart forever.

This ended Erietta's most important love affair—an affair she would never forget and would talk about to her children in years to come.

But all was not lost. This is not the end of Erietta's happiness. It does not stop at the love grown for this stranger whose name we do not know. And so, the story of Erietta begins.

Erietta Petropoulos in her older years.

The Constantinople Embassy Invitation

The year is 1901

The gathering was cosmopolitan. In addition to the high-ranking officials from other embassies were Italians, Swiss, French, Greeks and Americans, all holding their gold-edged invitations.

As their carriages swept up to the steps of the Embassy, they alighted, adjusting their sumptuous dresses, and prepared to make an entry which they hoped would be talked about for many a month after.

Now they all slowly began winding their way into the grand entrance hall. The ladies in their brilliant-coloured long dresses in all the colours of the rainbow looked like poetry in motion.

Dressed elegantly in velvet, satin, and silk, with bows, pearls and diamonds adorning their gowns, the ladies shimmered and shone like a cluster of butterflies in flight as they slowly moved forward towards the ornate wrought iron staircase, taking them to the ballroom upstairs.

It was a beautiful sight as they slowly swept up the marble steps, past the magnificent paintings on the walls.

Moving forward slowly, ever so slowly, the ladies held on tightly to their men's arms, who were conspicuous in their formal black attire and their colourful cummerbunds.

Here and there, the broad blue, green and mauve ribbon of some foreign order cut a dash across their breast. Some were adorned with medals which were held in place by colourful ribbons.

It was apparent the local dressmakers had been kept busy by the sea of elegantly dressed ladies now present for judging. This was the moment they had all been waiting for, the culmination of their anticipation.

People were slowly entering the ballroom now, with its marble pillars and its vast magnificent marble dance floor.

All around were strategically placed chaise lounges and ornate gold, red and blue velvet Louis XV chairs, which were intended for those wishing to sit whilst watching all those that took to the floor.

At the end of the ballroom, on a specially designed raised dais, the 22-piece orchestra was beginning to tune their instruments, adding another sound to the chattering, noisy, low hum of those already gathered there. Here and there, a bout of laughter erupted. It had the makings of a joyful gathering as everyone sought their friends to share the evening together.

The houseboys were darting around people, magnificent in their formal attire of pale blue tunics with gold braiding over their black trousers. Carrying the silver trays with champagne glasses and wearing the traditional red tarbouches (fez), they put the finishing touches to an already beautiful painting of those already gathered there.

A sudden hush came about. The ambassador had arrived. The orchestra poised and waited for the conductor to slowly lift his baton. Thus, the sound of music now flooded the whole room, greeting the ambassador with notes of fine instrumental masterpieces.

Everyone craned their neck to catch a glimpse of their host for the evening.

The couples took to the floor. Georgos, standing talking to his friends and their wives, was taking everything in. Everything was perfect. He was glad that he had come. His earlier misgivings were by now dispelled.

No one tonight could help but be happy amongst such an elegant gathering. The band was a lively one; everyone was smiling, and laughter was heard in abundance.

He waited for an opportune moment to walk around, greet a few more friends and put his name down for a few dances in the dance cards of the present young ladies.

Leisurely he strolled up to another group of friends that he had just caught sight of. Just as he was about to be introduced to a friend of theirs, he happened to glance opposite the room and there, standing next to a group of middle-aged men and two girls was the most gorgeous woman he had ever cast eyes on. She must have been about five foot three, with long chestnut brown hair that curled and reached her shoulders, held by a midnight blue broad ribbon in a mixture of satin and velvet.

Her green eyes were deep-set and almond-shaped. The eyes of scintillating emeralds, vivid and alive, and her long brown eyelashes served to emphasise the depths of their colour. A baby nose and a long, somewhat heart-shaped face made her appear different, mysterious, and exciting.

She wore a midnight blue velvet dress trimmed with a belt of the same shade in pleated satin, emphasising her neat and trim waist even more. But what made her stand out amongst this gathering of beautiful women was that she wore absolutely no adornments of any kind. There were no rings on her fingers, no necklaces of diamonds or pearls. She relied simply on her natural and youthful beauty, and in a room full of over-dressed women, she stood out with her utter simplicity.

Georgos' heart skipped a beat. Their eyes locked together for the briefest of moments, then Fani Christithou slowly and deliberately turned around, and with her back to Georgos now, started chatting to her two young companions. For in that brief split second, she had been captivated by that stranger across the room. There was a certain magnetism about him, a kind of restlessness as if he could take the world in one bout: a dynamic man indeed.

Obviously intrigued now, she asked her companions about him. Thus, she found out that Georgos Petropoulos, although quite a ladies' man, loved them and left them shortly after. Up to now none had lasted more than a few weeks, for, at the mere far sound of wedding bells, he ran like a hunted man.

It was Georgos' turn to find out more about her and was told by his friends that Mr Christithou had been an important embassy official in the Greek Embassy in France and that his only daughter, Fani, had been a border in one of the best French finishing schools. Her mother had died many years ago and her father never re-married, devoting his time entirely to his daughter and his work at the Embassy. These were the two loves in his life. He found out also that Fani's father aspired a son-in-law for his daughter within his circle.

He was sure that the lifestyle and travel that had for many years been their life would also be fit for Fani, his daughter.

Impetuously Georgos dragged along a friend who happened to know Mr Christithou to be officially introduced. The rest he knew would be and had to be up to him. As the introductions were made, Georgos found himself with a completely new feeling—nervousness. He just couldn't comprehend the state of his emotions. The usual 'hero poli' (pleased to meet you) took place with handshakes all around.

After making polite conversations with Mr Christithou, he turned round to Fani and asked her if she would reserve a dance or two for him. Fani made a point of studying her so far blank card. Deliberately she took her time, then, looking him straight in the eyes, quietly informed him that regretfully she only had one dance left, the very last one! He was stunned. Everyone knew it was just too early in the evening for the dance diaries to have been filled. Defiantly staring at him now, she dared him to contradict her. Those green eyes, boring through his very soul, made him feel like a chess opponent—waiting for his next move.

She had outmanoeuvred him, outfoxed him. Not only did they both know, but those around them too waited for the outcome. Nobody spoke. Georgos took the challenge. Throwing his head right back, he roared with laughter and, staring straight back at her, informed her that she was undoubtedly well worth the trouble of waiting for the last dance. And before she could say another word, he took the dance card from her in one swift motion and, with a flourish and a smile, put his name down for the last dance, in the otherwise blank card.

As time went by, Georgos and Fani found that their infatuation had turned from a fire to a blaze! Everyone, everywhere, loves a love story and there, for everyone to see, was such a love story unfolding. It was obvious to all that Georgos was smitten by Fani, so everyone conspired to help meet the two young people as often as possible.

They met everywhere.

They were included in elegant piano recitals, soirées, small dinner parties that every hostess loved to give, weddings, christenings, and name days.

For now, it was evident that this was not going to be one of the traditional arranged marriages. Any marriage matchmaker in their case was now surplus to requirements.

Both Georgos and Fani found that they had a lot in common—the same love for classical music, literature, poetry, and a great attraction to one another.

Georgos brought up the idea that women had a role to play within the home, and politics and decision-making matters were not part of a woman's role. Nevertheless, he thought Fani's ideas to be witty and worthy of consideration. Part of his love for her was that she was totally different from anyone he had ever met.

In the face of the obvious growing intimacy between the two, Fani's father had tried to persuade Fani that Georgos was not what he had wanted for her.

He did not move in the same circle that she had been used to. The likelihood of her ever travelling around the world as he had done in the past with his postings as an ambassador were nil.

Fani was adamant. She was happy now in Constantinople and had many friends. She did not crave travelling abroad, and although grateful to her father for the many years of love and happiness he had given her, she now wanted nothing more than to spend the rest of her life by Georgos' side.

She waited for Georgos to declare his love for her and then, as was the custom, to officially ask for her hand in marriage from her father.

She was sure that Georgos loved her. Every word, glance and gesture confirmed the fact to her.

Georgos and Fani

New Year's Eve

New Year's Eve found Georgos and Fani invited to an aunt's house for the celebrations.

This is a time once again for much drinking, merrymaking and the long-awaited 'Vassilopita' (Greek New Year Cake). Traditionally in olden times, there was a gold sovereign within the baked cake, and everyone knows luck follows the finder of the gold coin throughout the year.

The lucky coin was in Georgos' piece of Vassilopita. Egged by the cheering and clapping that followed, and in a euphoric state of mind, Georgos stood up and held Fani's gaze for a long while, then addressing Fani's father, declared his love, and formally asked for her hand in marriage.

A great commotion erupted. No one waited for the traditional "yes" from the father. Congratulations were flying from all quarters, so noisy that no one really took any notice of her father's silence.

Fani did, though, and quietly slipping from her chair, went towards her father and, putting her arms around him, kissed him softly and murmured, "Efharisto Baba" (thanks, Daddy) and "S'agapo" (I love you).

This officially began the courtship of Georgos and Fani, and whilst waiting for the date to be fixed for the engagement, the father spoke with a go-between and arranged for the dowry that he would bestow for Fani that would enhance the couple's status within the community. They would have a home for everyone to admire, and of course, the richer the father was, the bigger the dowry and the better the home would be.

For the young couple now being engaged was both an exciting and a special time too, not only for getting to know one another but for making plans and for the deep secret whisperings of "I love you" that lovers all over the world exchange.

With the advent of the engagement and the wedding taking place within the year, the merry-go-round of preparations took place.

The date for the wedding, the choice of 'koumbaros' (best man), the dressmaker; all of it had to be found. The dressmaker would also be very busy indeed producing the trousseau, the dresses, costumes, evening gowns and last but not least, the wedding dress itself.

Georgos, too, would leave the parental home and create a new home and a new life as Georgos, the husband.

Henceforth, his parents would take second place in all and everything in his life.

Slowly the knot will untie, and the young man will be free to devote his entire life to someone who, until recently, was a stranger to all.

The mother who had carried her precious son for nine months, sat up nights when he was ill, worried over his future, now was to play a secondary role in his life.

The untying of the knot that held her precious son would be accomplished seemingly in happiness and joy. No one was allowed to witness the final emotional handing over. If tears were to be shed, she must do so silently and privately. Nothing and no one must be allowed to mar his happiness.

The nearer the time was for the wedding, the dearer Fani's friends became. She knew, once married, they would not and could not play a significant role in her life. The cocoon which had wrapped her in her father's house would no longer hold her. In its place, a mantle of responsibility to husband and home would forever be hers.

A new, mysterious, and unknown life lay ahead of her. Daunting though it seemed, she was glad that at least she had been the one to choose the man she so deeply loved and was prepared to spend the rest of her life with him.

In Constantinople at the time, there were many tarot card readers, tellers of fortune, and one such was Kiria Charalambou, so-called 'Flitzanou'—being that she read the future in the bottom of coffee cups. The dredges of the Greek coffee, when finished, were swirled around the cup, and turned upside down onto the saucer. After a few seconds, the pattern that was formed was interpreted by the Flitzanou.

On one such afternoon, Fani decided to visit this Greek fortune teller. She had heard many friends say how excellent her readings were, and being so near her marriage, she decided to have a go at seeing what her future held. Secretly with two of her friends, she went on her way. Her father called all such tellers of fortune 'charlatans'. This only added to the excitement of the girls. Her two friends had gone in separately. It was now Fani's turn. Having drunk the Greek coffee in the usual small cup, she sat back and waited for the outcome with quiet anticipation. Kiria Charalambou took a while, turning the small cup one way and another. Fani's heart was beating quite strongly in her chest. She could not wait.

At last, the Flitzanou looked up and said, "Your cup is too murky for the reading—I cannot make out a lot of things." she muttered, "All I can say is that in the future, a lot of bitter tears will be shed."

The Flitzanou's findings were to become of considerable importance within this story.

She seemed to be in a hurry to get rid of Fani and couldn't wait to lead her gently to the door. Fani offered to pay, but she would not accept any payment. "I haven't been able to see anything", she finished by saying.

Her friends were waiting to hear what Kiria Charalambou had to say. They too, were puzzled and told Fani how accurate and well informed their readings were.

With a shrug of the shoulders, Fani and her friends decided that Kiria Charalambou must have been tired or maybe late for an appointment, and the episode was forgotten—for now! Fani treasured those precious moments she had with her friends, for it was not long until she was about to venture into the next chapter of her life—marriage.

A small gathering took place, where Fani's friends of many years, some since her school days, had come to bid her the fondest of farewells, for in the bottom of their hearts, henceforth, Fani's friendships would take second place, once married. Then, nothing ever remains the same.

Na Zisete

The koumbaros was chosen.

The koumbaros is so much more than just the best man. In the eyes of the Greek Orthodox Church, he will henceforth be the 'prostatis'—the protector of the new couple.

He will also stand as Godfather to the couples' first child, being on hand to help during the child's life and even provide financial help towards their education, if required.

The best man was chosen after giving much thought, and there was careful consideration as to who the couple selected. In the eyes of the Greek community and its people, it was indeed an honour to be asked to be a koumbaros.

The Greek Orthodox Church that day was beautifully decked out with fresh flowers. All around was the sweet smelling of jasmines, lilies, roses, and heliotropes, all bunched and draped with white ribbons, on every pew, nestling above the altar, cascading from vases everywhere.

White five-foot candles shimmered and shone with dazzling white and silver threaded ribbons with tiny flowers winding their way to the top of the thick stems.

Greek weddings usually take place at sundown when the exhausting heat of the day gives way to the coolness of early evening.

For now, everything was silent, watchful, awaiting the bursts of guests that were to arrive. The church lights would shimmer through the myriads of lights projected from their chandeliers, casting shadows and half-light onto the icons all around the church.

As the bride would enter, holding onto her father's arm, the gigantic candles and lights would blend with the festoon of flowers, giving out a picture of fantasy and beauty in step with the happiness radiated by everyone gathered therein.

The sugared almonds 'koufeta' in pink and white nets gathered with tiny ribbons in a multitude of rainbow colours, nestled together like tiny fairy ballerinas. Each bunch of koufeta had an inscription of the bride and groom's name with the date of their marriage inside. They would be distributed to every guest on their way out of the church as a testimony to the wedding they had just attended.

The very important 'stefana' or marriage garlands are woven from small fragrant white waxy lemon blossom flowers, and the two garlands tied together with white satin ribbon are symbolic of the joining 'together' of the couple for life. Those stefana were now waiting too by the altar.

A couple is not truly married until the stefana crowns or garlands have been exchanged over their heads by the priest during the ceremony.

The simple gold wedding rings were then put on their fingers by the priest after a brief blessing.

The couple now wore their wedding rings inscribed with each other's names and the wedding date.

The couple is now married in the eyes of the Greek Orthodox Church. There is much kissing and hand-shaking for the bride and groom from every guest with the words 'Na Zisete' (may you live long) before proceeding to the exit with their customary koufeta in their hands.

In the evening, the bride and groom have the first dance together, then the father takes his turn with his daughter for a dance. Then, one by one, everyone joins in.

As each man finishes his dance, he will throw some money on the ground for the newlyweds.

In Cyprus, it is customary for everyone to go up to the bride and pin money in notes all over her dress. When her wedding dress is full, she is called aside by her mother, who proceeds to unpin the money and put it aside. Once again, everyone continues to pin more money to the dress.

In Crete, as in some parts of Corfu, gunshots are fired as a sign of rejoicing too.

Georgos and Fani went through the Greek Orthodox ceremony and, in the eyes of the church and the people gathered there, started their life as man and wife.

They were very much in love; they had the rest of their lives in front of them.

Or so they thought—events were to prove otherwise.

Fani and Georgos settled into their new life as a married couple.

They widened their circle of friends, gave small intimate dinner parties, attended gatherings and were very much in demand, both for their beauty as a couple, their wit, and the very radiance of their love for all to see.

Slowly Georgos was building up his business as an architect. They wanted for nothing. They were happy and ready to start a family.

On 8th March 1903, their joy was complete. Fani gave birth to a baby boy, their firstborn, whom they named Diamandis Alexandros. To Georgos, this meant a continuance of the Petropoulos line, and to a Greek, a son for the first child was indeed a good omen and a proud moment!

Diamandis, or Damy as he was nicknamed, was followed on 20th June 1904 by a little sister named Erietta. She was a lovely little girl with piercing green eyes and a sunshine disposition. Like any proud parents, this moment, too, was sheer magic. The family was now complete.

The love of Georgos and Fani knew no bounds. She would have followed him to the ends of the earth. As far as Georgos was concerned, Fani was the epitome of everything he had ever desired or wanted in his life. She was his very existence.

In the midst of an important assignment, Georgos would suddenly be seized with an inexplicable fear, a desire to rush and see that all was well with his family. He would leave everything, and dashing home, would crazily embrace and hug Fani, and twirl Damy and Erietta high, high above his head. He loved them all dearly.

Fani was used to such demonstrations, spontaneous and crazy, for she would suddenly wake up in the middle of the night with an urge to cradle Georgos and her children tight, tight against her.

They both knew how lucky they were and how much life had bestowed upon them. They never took anything for granted for a moment, and Fani would often dash to church and, kneeling, would give grateful thanks for her lovely family and light a candle as she left the church.

In Search of a Better Life

Fani and Georgos had talked long and late, night after night. Their koumbaros, godfather, as well as many friends, had left Constantinople for Alexandria. They had so enthusiastically described the way of life, and the money that was to be made too. This was a land of opportunity and plenty.

Georgos, young and wanting more—oh so much more for his family—decided to emigrate to Alexandria after Fani's complete consent and a lot of soul-searching.

He would work hard, build a new home, and call his family in time to join him.

Fani's dowry had been wisely invested. Greeks value having something put aside for a rainy day. Many save from the very first day of the birth of their children in order to give them a home, education and comfort.

Georgos knew as he stood by the Quay with his family that the point of no return was now. The first step taken on the ladder of life was to reach out for the fruition of all his dreams and plans.

Standing alone on the deck now and with the full impact of the separation upon him like a tight steel rod around his chest, he felt for a moment the first twinges of uncertainty.

The boat had slowly crept out of the harbour with Fani and the children left behind, now just specks on the horizon.

Sitting on his tiny bed in a cabin holding twenty people, Georgos, with reason prevailing and emotions still tearing him apart, vowed to make a go and quickly so, in this new land of opportunity.

He knew he had to live up to Fani's faith in him and her generous acquiescence of his dream of a prosperous future for all of them.

Alexandria

A year had gone by. Georgos had worked hard, made many useful contacts, and had a wide circle of friends and associates.

His marriage to Fani with her father's embassy connections had in many ways got him into the 'set' he wanted to be in, and this helped his career to no end.

He had invested the dowry in building a beautiful and desirable villa in Sidi Gaber, a quiet and opulent suburb of Alexandria.

Using the mind's eye, we can understand how he was lured to this rich capital city of Alexandria (Arabic name: Al Iskandrarīyah), founded in 332 B.C. by Alexander the Great.

A steady influx of Greeks, Italians, French and English had turned it into a European city, complete with wide avenues, the best of schools, operas, casinos, banks, and elegant buildings.

There were servants and cooks. Nearly every European had a live-in help. Their wages were low, for Egyptians themselves lived in near poverty, unlike the Europeans there.

Alexandria, in other words, was a place where one could prosper and live a very comfortable life indeed.

All-in-all, Georgos was a deeply contented man. He had built a beautiful home for Fani and the children, who would be arriving soon. He had worked hard and couldn't wait to show Fani what he had achieved for all of them.

The day his family was due to arrive, he spent most of the afternoon bent over his drawing board designing a luxurious home for a prominent Italian solicitor who had married a countess with substantial money to invest.

Tiredness had penetrated every bone in his body, and coupled with his earlier boredom, the days were not going quickly enough before his family could join him. Every minute was an hour, and if it hadn't been for his work, he would have gone crazy.

He decided that what he needed was a breath of fresh air to blow the cobwebs away. He was sure that would bring back the happy mood that he very much needed.

He stepped outside and saw the sun was still shining. The late afternoon had brought along with it a hint of a promise of a gentle breeze. Just then, a horse-drawn carriage passed by. Georgos stopped him, alighted the carriage and instructed the driver to go around the Corniche (the Embankment).

Slowly and leisurely, the carriage wound its way around, first passing the yacht club, then a small fishing port, who's brightly painted little boats bobbed up and down like tiny gnomes with colourfully painted hats.

Then, from his comfortable leather seat, his eyes focused on the jetty with its fishing nets hanging out to dry, like some gigantic spider's web.

Passing the majestic Fort of Quaitbay on the western tip of the headland, he observed the warm reds and oranges of an Alexandrian sunset turning the old sandstone building of the fort into the colour of rich honey—gooey and warm.

The scenery and gentle clippety-clop sound of the horses' hooves as they sped along cobbled streets slowly soothed away his tiredness.

Now intent on enjoying the scenery around him, he observed the laughing, happy people sitting at sidewalk tables.

Driver and passenger were now passing the Pharos (lighthouse) of Alexandria, one of the Seven Wonders of the Ancient World.

Georgos' admiration at this piece of the historical wonder of by-gone days knew no bounds. He was never tired of remembering its past history, and although the structure itself as it had been, long since disappeared and in its place now the fort, the then King of Egypt Ptolemy II, decreed that henceforth it would be called Pharos. The fort incorporated some of the Pharos' debris and housed the naval museum in the harbour of the Island of Pharos. Built in 279 B.C., it was the largest of its kind and the word Pharos then came to be used in many languages meaning 'lighthouse'. It stood over four hundred feet tall. Its square base had housed around three hundred rooms for operators and mechanics.

Above had been octagonal, then a circular storey topped by a lantern with a beacon which the books described as a mirror of polished steel to reflect the sun by day and moon by night. This suggested some kind of lens or mirror.

Many stories and legends have emerged about the huge lens mirror housed at the lighthouse's summit. It was said that its powerful rays and the sun's rays would turn upon enemy ships approaching the harbour, and just like a burning glass that children use to start a small fire, it would destroy them!

Invigorated by the scenery from the comfort of his seat, Georgos' tiredness vanished as if by magic. He reached the end of his stroll around the Corniche, and thanking the driver, entered his home.

Once inside, he looked around, trying to visualise it through the eyes of his beloved wife, who would be joining him soon. He took a deep breath and let it out slowly. He felt wonderful. Everything had gone his way. All the dreams and hopes he had planned with Fani had materialised. Life was worth living—he felt that fate was definitely by his side.

Fani's arrival with their children was a very emotional reunion, and soon before long, it was as if they had never been away. Fani enjoyed being by her husband's side, and the children settled into their new home with new adventures awaiting them.

Preparations for Easter

The year is 1910

Sunlight slowly filtered through the closed afternoon shutters; the air outside held promise of a cool afternoon breeze.

Fani stood inside her beautiful kitchen. She was busy preparing and baking the traditional Greek Easter bread called 'Tsourekia'. The Tsourekia are made from sweet yeast dough with aniseed, water, sugar, eggs, and flour. They are made in many shapes and sizes—some like dolls and some plaited, but always with a red Easter egg baked in the middle. Mothers usually bake one for each child in the family in various designs and shapes.

The red Easter eggs, symbolic of the red blood of Christ, which constitute a significant part of Easter Sunday, were also being prepared. They are hard-boiled, then dyed with a special red powder dye.

Whilst all the joyful Easter preparations were taking place, Fani was intensely aware of how lucky she was. She had settled quite well since arriving from Constantinople, just over two years before. She quickly got used to Alexandria—the easy-going way of life, a kind of 'dolce vita'. They took part in many gatherings, outings, and home entertainments. Fani and Georgos befriended many people, especially because there were so many Greeks living there. They had a servant too, a live-in Egyptian girl called Fatma, who certainly was of tremendous help with everything.

Damy was by now seven years old. A tall, sturdy boy who attended school and was in every way a good scholar. It was Georgos' most desired ambition to have his son follow in his footsteps as an architect.

Would that happen? Only the future would tell.

Daydreaming, Fani finished her housework and most of the Easter preparations. It was hot, very hot, but it was considerably cooler at sunset. This was when the family would enjoy their evening meals on the veranda, which led to the garden. With a million stars overhead and the heavenly scent of all the flowers, this was as close to perfection as anyone could imagine.

Fani loved her garden. It was her pride and joy, and she had spent many hours planning and planting there. For the Petropoulos family, as for the rest of the Greeks, it was the final week of lent and fasting. Most Greeks observe the forty days of fasting during which no meat or fish passes their mouths.

In the windows of her mind now, Fani visualised the sacred Easter pageant that Paraskevie—her lifelong friend, married now and living in Corfu—and her family would be attending at the square near the Liston, in the heart of Corfu town.

All around the square, from the ground floor to the top of all the historical buildings, balconies had been covered in red cloths—as far as the eye could see, a sea of red—symbolic of the blood of Christ.

Easter celebrations in Corfu, Greece.

From within the balconies, friends and relatives were standing—some balconies holding some twenty to thirty people—holding urns, jugs, pottery, and large pots filled with water.

The police had cleared the area around the balconies, and the town clocks struck midday. Suddenly the hush was broken with an almighty series of bangs and clatter, as hundreds of the urns and pottery from all around the balconies were thrown down onto the square. They had chosen today to show their anger and vent their displeasure towards Judas, who had betrayed Christ. Like a series of machine guns, the urns smashed and clattered on the ground below—the crowds were standing well back now, joining in clapping and shouting 'naí' (yes).

The people of Kerkyra (Corfu) had not been allowed to forget their evil Judas. They had visually partaken, felt and shown their feelings. Slowly and silently now the crowd dispersed. Saturday midnight—the expectation was in the air. The melancholy felt by all on Good Friday was slowly giving way to hope. Suddenly all those attending midnight mass in their thousands awaited the moment silently when, after plunging the church into total darkness, the priest emerged with one single bright light— the consecrated one! The light had been brought from the tomb of the Greek Orthodox Church in Jerusalem.

"Come and receive the light," proclaimed the priest.

All hell broke loose. Church bells rang and the hooting from cars, boats and yachts all added to the din of the people cheering. Rockets, fireworks, and Roman candles added their noise and colour to the night sky. As the consecrated light was passed on from one person to another, everyone rushed to have their candle lit. The priest chanted "Christós Anésti" (Christ is risen). The procession of thousands of people slowly winding their way home with their lit candles flickering created a magical picture.

Arriving on the doorstep of one's home, the Easter flame, the consecrated one from Jerusalem that cupped hands had carefully carried whilst it still flickered, gently made the sign of the cross above the entrance door. The imprint of the blackened cross made by the Easter candle remains visible for many months henceforth, and it is presumed to be a good omen too!

An Easter Tragedy

Easter Sunday in the beautiful gardens of Sidi Gaber, home to Fani and Georgos and their children, Damy and Erietta, was this morning the sight and sound of much merrymaking that could be clearly heard from afar.

In the large front garden, the many children of the guests had now gathered and joined Damy and Erietta. The children were happily playing all kinds of games, clearly not interested in the merrymaking taking place in the back garden. Adults were of no interest in the children's world.

The children all waited with great excitement for when the fireworks and Roman candles would be let off. But that part comes later as a grand finale when the feasting and the merrymaking are over.

In the back garden, numerous tables had been laid under the shade of the lemon and orange trees. The beautiful white damask tablecloths covering the tables were in sharp contrast to the many red Easter eggs that had been placed in crystal bowls on the tables.

The two lambs were slowly being turned on the spit. The smell from the charcoal, mingled with the smell from the herbs and marinade, filled the air with smoke and such pungent, mouth-watering smells that made each and everyone there—guest and family alike—feel unashamedly weak from hunger.

The flowers scattered around the garden vied with the beautiful and colourful dresses of those ladies present. One of the guests had brought along an accordion, another a mandolin—the instrument loved and used by many Greeks. This plucked instrument has four double courses of wire strings tuned in the same way as a violin. It is played with a plectrum, using a tremolo effect to sustain longer notes.

As one song died away, another began, with the accordion and mandolin each taking turns, and everyone joining in the singing.

For at this moment in the beautiful gardens of Fani and Georgos, there was indeed an air of happiness. All the guests had 'kefi' (good mood). A plethora of sound, smell, and vision, equal to nothing on earth.

This Easter gathering was indeed a great success.

Among the many guests gathered there this beautiful sunny Easter Sunday, many could not help but be envious of Fani, Georgos and their loving family. Damy was now seven, and Erietta six. She was a green-eyed girl, happy and chirpy and the apple of her father's eye. Damy adored his little sister and protected her as a big brother. Both children were so dearly loved.

Erietta and Damy as young children.

Of course, they envied Georgos and his meteoric rise to being one of the most sought-after architects in Alexandria after such a short while having left Constantinople. Oh, how they envied the ability of this happy family who seemingly had everything!

Little did everyone gathered there know then that as the minutes were ticking away so slowly, a tragedy would strike. A tragedy so destructive that would leave in its wake a trail of grief and misery, tearing asunder husband and family and casting them into a holocaust of grief and sorrow, with no reprieve.

In Greek mythology, in the realm of those Greek gods on Mount Olympus, it was thought then that on no account should one attract the attention of the gods by any sign or portrayal of happiness. Only the gods, it was said, were completely and utterly happy—not the humans!

You still hear the phrase 'touch wood', or in Italian 'toca legno', or in Greek 'ktipa ksilo', because who knows what might happen. A wise man once said, "There is nothing wrong with a little bit of extra insurance."

While the parents were busy preparing for the big Easter feasting, the children gathered in the front garden were getting somewhat bored. They had played all the games they knew, invented a few more, sang all the songs, fought a little, made new friends, exchanged childish secrets, and the girls had teased and tormented the boys, calling each other names. Threats of "I'll tell your Dad, Mum, Aunty" had long ceased to create a stimulus. What now?

Damy had been picked and appointed spokesman by all the children to inquire as to when the fireworks would begin, perhaps even to hasten their start. Feeling grown up and very important, Damy, just seven years old, went to his mother to request that they all wanted the fireworks to begin.

He quickly returned to his friends with the answer they had not wanted to hear— "Later." That word is so much in use by adults. We are all guilty of using this magic word to substitute "Go away", but what does it mean exactly? Later? In an hour? A day? Half a day? Tomorrow?

Feeling let down and facing all those children, knowing that he had failed in his grown-up mission and had achieved precisely nothing, Damy decided to take matters into his own hands. "What is the harm?" "Why not?" Nobody would find out, he hoped.

Bravely, and feeling like a hero within this circle of children, he marched into the house where he knew the fireworks were stored in readiness for the display. He seized two Roman candles, fat and colourful. Dashing now into the kitchen, he seized a box of matches and, quickly stuffing his treasure trove into his pockets, proceeded for the front garden, where all his friends were waiting for him.

Once amongst their midst, he quickly and proudly showed his acquisition. He felt like a hero. The children all around him thought so, too. Two of the children stood guard near the narrow-paved edge that divided the front garden from the back, whilst Damy proceeded to light the Roman candle. Slowly and carefully, he lit it and stood back. Nothing happened. No fizz, no colourful display, no noise. Just a little smouldering smoke. Such a disappointment! Damy, feeling a little crestfallen now, picked the candle up and put it in his pocket. "That was not much fun," shouted the children.

He quickly put the second Roman candle firmly on the grass and lit it. Whoosh! Wham! Bang! This one was a beauty. What colours, what a spectacular display. The children clapped, whilst they took another look-out towards the adult world on the other side of the garden. Nothing. Nobody had noticed anything. The singing and accordion had drowned the whoosh of the Roman candle. Suddenly Damy felt heat coming from his trouser pocket. The pocket felt burning. He put his hand in and felt the skin burning right through his thumb. He quickly withdrew his hand. In a flash, the children caught sight of Damy's trousers, now well and truly alight. They started screaming and pointing at him. The box of matches was quickly lit by the smouldering candle that lay in his pocket.

Damy felt the heat through the cloth. He panicked and tried to run. The wrong thing to do, but just pure panic had set upon him. He just wanted to escape the heat and the flame. The children started to run towards the back garden where the adults were to seek help. They were hysterical, shouting "Fotiá, fotiá" (fire, fire) whilst jumping up and down.

Still in their own noisy world, the adults thought it was just another prank, a childish game they were playing, and continued with the merrymaking. Fani looked up instinctively, and her heart beating tightly against her chest, took hold of a child as panic set in. She shook her to find out exactly what was going on.

Something told her that she was not witnessing a children's game but something dire. "Damy! Damy!" the children cried. Lifting her long skirts, she ran towards the front garden, where the sight of Damy's trousers in flames greeted her and made her freeze for a moment.

Terror gave way to practicality. Seizing him firmly against her, she enveloped him in her arms and slowly, slowly, suffocated the flames. Realising his fright and sheer terror, she kept him tightly in her arms for a moment longer.

That was a mistake—a mistake that would cost her dearly. For she hadn't realised that the flames that had left Damy now licked their way slowly and were getting a hold on her numerous and voluminous skirts and petticoats. By the time realisation dawned, she herself was set alight!

Georgos ran towards her clutching a damask tablecloth one of the guests had thrust in his hands, which had adorned the Easter table earlier. Wrapping the tablecloth around her, he held her tightly in his arms whilst kneeling.

The acrid smell of burnt flesh reached the onlookers, and they all knew without being told the severity of the burns that Fani had encountered. Like a crazy slow-motion nightmare, Georgos stood holding Fani in the tablecloth—the same tablecloth that had held the red eggs and food that very morning—which was slowly turning into a charcoal colour rag.

The woman inside the tablecloth was now beyond recognition. Black bits of skin had stuck to her clothes, making grotesque patterns of lumps of burnt flesh intermingled with burnt cloth. What was flesh, and what was cloth? Her hair, her beautiful hair, looked like a burnt rag doll that had been thrown in the fire and retrieved at the last moment.

Georgos crooned and moaned, and his moans mingled with hers. His tears which he kept brushing away from time to time with his dusty charcoal hands, were leaving an imprint similar to a clown's makeup—a clown that had shed tears and was now a mask of grotesque facial patterns.

Then the screams started from the figure huddled and lying in Georgos' arms. They were inhuman screams, gut-dash ripping moans like that of an animal caught in a trap.

From the frozen group of guests and bystanders, a friend emerged—a doctor. The eyes that stared at him were red and bloodshot, but Fani could see through them. He tried to examine her, feel a pulse, but the creature-like person who stared and moaned was now, in his opinion, beyond the reach of any human help. Pieces of charred bones were visible. An ambulance was called, and a doctor came with it. All he could do was to give her morphine. Even that was just a gesture—it didn't help. Some of her internal organs had perished. The morphine could not find its way through the human canals.

The ambulance doors now closed. The now life-ebbing and pain-riddled woman, beautiful and lively only minutes earlier, was taken away—away from the children she had loved and brought into the world and the home she had lovingly created. This was to be her last journey.

Haros (Death)

Haros makes no concession on his final round.

The children remained behind as the ambulance sped away. Tearful, perplexed and choking with emotion, they went into the house to be looked after by caring neighbours, friends, and relatives.

In hospital now, Georgos knelt by Fani's bed and no longer crying, crooned, and sung to her. He felt she needed him more than ever. He would transmit by voice and touch a love that was welling inside him, churning him, and threatening to choke him. He wanted to die right there beside her. Right now, nothing else or no one mattered to him apart from his beloved.

Ironically, a few hours beforehand, Fani had followed the Easter Mass and taken part in the solemnity and the agony of the dying Christ on the cross. Little knowing then that her own agony, pain and anguish were yet to start.

After three long days and nights, silently and swiftly like a thief in the night, Haros crept and claimed the lovely young woman.

Haros had not only taken a mother, but he had also taken a beloved wife, snatching her from the arms of a husband

and two children who adored her and were utterly devastated.

Deep into the night after Georgos returned home after Fani had drawn her last tortured breath, the children heard another sound from their father's bedroom.

A sound of their father sobbing softly—dry tearless sobs that seemed to come from the very depth of his soul. His love for Fani had not had the time to grow stale and become ordinary.

The sound of their mother's inhuman moans and the human sounds of their father's sobs were to remain in the children's memory for the rest of their lives.

It was branded on their soul with an emotional red-hot iron.

A Bid Farewell

Fani was buried in Alexandria not on a cold, wind-swept day but on a bright warm day with the beaming sun overhead. Nature was not mourning!

The emotional goodbye at the cemetery and the giving away of her body was a living nightmare for Georgos.

Holding Damy and Erietta tightly by the hand, he bid her farewell and returned to their home—a home she would no longer be there to share with them.

Fani was buried in accordance with the Greek Orthodox rites. The Requiem 'Mnimosino' (the memorial service), which takes place forty days after death, was equally traumatic for all.

Of the many friends that gathered that day at the Requiem for the last farewell, two remembered Kiria Charalambou—that Greek coffee-shop fortune-teller who had refused to see Fani's future in her cup. Was it truly just that she had somewhere else to go that day, that she was in a hurry, or was it simply that she had foreseen the horrendous tragedy in Fani's cup? Was it a coincidence that events that followed were perhaps too sad to pass on? Nevertheless, the episode brought to the surface remained in their minds for a long, long time.

Georgos' life now continued, but he merely existed, and this was only because of his children. He felt somewhat a kind of living dead. Nothing mattered, and nothing existed beyond the walls of his home.

Late at night, in the utter silence, lying awake in the bedroom he and Fani had once shared, memories cascaded and crowded through his mind, caving in on him and chasing sleep away.

Fani's death seemed final. The Flitzanou had predicted her fate. Haros had swooped and claimed another victim, like the grim reaper in the night, thirsty and hungry for death. Tradition states that the name of a person who dies under tragic circumstances should not be bestowed upon another living person. It was a fact that the name Fani now carried with it bad luck, a curse one might say, never to be used again. It was to be buried and never dug up. After all, Fani was burnt—the flames engulfed her whole body, leaving her a mere shell of what she used to be. Once disturbed, the repercussions would be ten-fold.

Just like the sacred tomb of King Tutankhamun of Ancient Egypt who remained for three thousand years— once this long-lost tomb was disturbed, a deadly curse was awakened, and Haros once again caused mass destruction. As legend suggests, the tomb was inscribed with "Death shall come on swift wings to him that toucheth the tomb of a Pharaoh". Reportedly, a hawk was seen flying over the Valley of the Kings on the day that Howard Carter found the tomb in 1922. This was considered a bad omen, perhaps a warning from the other side. The greatest discovery of all time was riddled with vengeance and tragedy, claiming the lives of thirteen associates.

Why did the tomb have to be disturbed? Were the many deaths truly linked? One will never know.

Despite the warnings, the name of Fani was given to the daughter of Erietta, the twin of Maria. She was often nicknamed 'Fanoula'. She wanted the family name to live on, despite its harrowing past. Just like the fire that burnt Fani alive, a horrific fall changed the life of young Fani. After falling out of her nanny's arms, Fanoula plummeted down a flight of marble stairs like a lifeless ragdoll caught in a whirlwind. Although she survived, her life was changed forever, and she was never the same again. What should have been a carefree childhood for Fanoula was snatched away from her and replaced with major brain surgery and epilepsy. Fanoula, in her adult years, went into a home where she was happy and content. She had a love for Greek coffee, handbags and a good game of cards. She was very popular and had lots of friends. Although very much loved and cared for, Fanoula died at the age of seventy-four.

Fanoula enjoying a cup of Greek coffee and cake.

The curse of the name followed the family through history. A name that should never have been resurrected. Just like Tutankhamun, his tomb should have remained sealed and undisturbed.

Haros twitched once more—could he claim yet another victim?

Life Goes On

Georgos with his children, Damy (left) and Erietta (right) in mourning attire in 1910, after the death of Fani.

The once loving family, home, and routine that Fani had created was replaced with unruliness and freedom with no direction. A tiger released into the wild, without any direction and boundaries, will run free.

The children left behind, orphaned, and bereft of their darling mother had a succession of nannies over time. They came and went, one worse than the other. A stranger simply could not replace the love of a mother! With no mistress to supervise them and a master engulfed in a world of grief, they had a field day and did whatever they wanted. Although he loved his children dearly, he simply could not replace the warmth and motherly love of Fani. If only Georgos could turn over a new leaf on the calendar of his life and part with the hurt and pain of losing Fani. He knew that would never be the case as long as he lived and that he would continue to carry all his emotional despair forever like a piece of unwanted luggage.

Although Georgos' heart always would remain with Fani, a while later he met a French lady, who was known as Tante (Aunt) Marie throughout the family. Marie was an attractive, chic, kind, and good-natured woman. They were happy and the children loved her. She would lovingly sit on the rocking chair with one of the children on her lap, rocking and singing songs until they fell asleep. But, sadly the relationship wasn't meant to last long. The family's disapproval drove Marie to leave and in return, Georgos was introduced to Maria Rigopoulos who was seen as a more suitable alternative as a wife and the person who would mother the children.

Georgos and Maria met through the intermediary of the time-honoured marriage arranger. Georgos hoped that the children would have in Maria a substitute mother, not only for their needs but also to be the stabiliser in his household, for he knew how much a mother's love was important in both Damy and Erietta's life.

In exchange, he would provide for the Rigopoulos family, who were respectful and highly regarded in the eyes of the Greek community, but financially penniless now. He would give Maria, Eleni, her sister, and Nicolas, their brother, all the financial help they required. Maria and Eleni were not against marriage as an institution, but having gone through their youth looking after Nicolas, now twenty-five years old, they never felt the need or desire to marry.

Maria was tall and thin, always elegantly dressed, with the best quality clothes. She had a very prominent nose that emphasised her sharp angular features and piercingly sharp eyes that seemed to look right through the soul as if all your secrets and lies were easily accessible materials to her. She was a great believer in discipline and hard work; a sharp contrast to Fani's natural loving motherly ways.

Maria Rigopoulos

Eleni, a nondescript wishy-washy person, was at her happiest away from the limelight and people. She was never comfortable around others.

Now, mistress of the Petropoulos household, Maria began by laying down the foundations of the children's education.

Damy was sent to a public school that catered for children with an above-average ability, which according to his teachers, Damy possessed.

Of course, Georgos' dearest wish was that Damy would follow in his footsteps and train to be an architect like him.

Erietta, on the other hand, was sent to one of the best finishing schools for young ladies. Notre Dame de Sion was run by nuns with an emphasis on discipline and hard work. Those beliefs were held so dear by Maria herself.

The girls were force-fed a diet of literature and books. They learnt to speak rapidly and beautifully in French, Italian, German, English and Greek and learned to play the piano to something approaching concert level. This made provision for them to be accomplished in numerous skills and have extensive interests in worldwide affairs, to justify the extortionate amount of money the parents had to pay.

In fact, they were taught the social niceties, for naturally, these girls were required to sparkle within the Greek community.

Nicolas Rigopoulos

Nicolas Rigopoulos was the youngest and worked as a salesman. He was handsome, outgoing and a brilliant conversationalist. He could charm the birds off the trees, and it wasn't the feathered kind he charmed so often!

He loved his job, which enabled him to indulge in his hobby of being well-dressed in smart and expensive clothes, which gave him the opportunity to meet different people from all walks of life. He loved to flirt. The name of the game was being successful with women. He loved them all and had many girlfriends, and rumour had it he had many mistresses too!

That in itself was no big deal, except for the fact that Nicolas was a family man. He was married with two children—Sassa, who was ten years old, and a baby boy called Constatinos or Costas for short. As was the Greek tradition, he was named after the father of the father. Costas was a beautiful blond, blue-eyed boy adored by his father. Maria and Eleni also spoilt him and pampered to his every whim.

The wife of Nicolas, Caterina, was a plain but good Greek girl and a marvellous housewife and mother.

Lately, she had been suffering from a severe case of 'melancholia' or depression after the birth of Costas.

It did not help matters that Nicolas was a philanderer. She could not avoid being aware of it. Nicolas made no bones about it. He was a larger than life type of character, gregarious and loved having fun with the ladies. Caterina, on the other hand, being plain, shy, and retiring, was the complete antithesis of her husband. Oh, how she longed to be beautiful, intelligent, and witty—all the qualities she thought Nicolas looked for and sought in women.

Alas, that was not so. Her state of depression grew even deeper.

Finally, on the advice of their doctor, who had known the family for many years, and after talks with Maria and Eleni, Nicolas decided that the best thing to do was take his wife on her own with him on a short sea cruise from Alexandria to Greece.

The children Sassa and Costas were to be looked after by Maria and Eleni.

He sincerely hoped that the sea air coupled with the 'bonhomie' (cheerfulness) that usually existed amongst people on cruises would swiftly shake her melancholy away.

He had miscalculated. This timid, neurotic woman was possessed with extreme jealousy. She would go through long crying spells where she shut herself off in her room and cried away all her real and imaginary pain.

She tried her best to mingle and mix during her sea cruise and enjoy her evening with Nicolas and the people aboard the ship. But if the truth were known, she detested every minute of every hour.

Nicolas tried to be gentle and kind to her, tried to make her feel a part of him. And oh, he tried, he truly tried to curb his flirting.

It was no good, women were attracted to him like moths to a light, and somehow all his earlier resolutions were oh so quickly forgotten.

The night before they arrived in Greece, most of the people on the cruise had gathered to spend the last evening before docking, playing the piano, singing and of course merrily drinking the hours away in good company and before the early morning landing.

Not so for Caterina. She pleaded a severe headache and retired to her cabin.

Nicolas went after her and tried in vain to persuade her to join the crowd. Not having succeeded, he made sure she was comfortable in bed, kissed her goodnight and left her to join the party where all the fun was.

In the early hours of the morning, everyone proceeded to retire and catch a few hours of sleep before reaching Greece.

But when Nicolas tried to get into his cabin, he found he was unable to do so. It was as if something was blocking the door. Panic-stricken, Nicolas gave the door an almighty heave, and it gave way. Their trunk with all the clothes had been pushed against the door. Looking up, Nicolas caught sight of a weird shape—it was Caterina. She had hung herself!

The ship carrying the couple on what had started off as a second honeymoon now returned silently, mournfully, with a coffin on deck.

Haros had claimed another life. Maybe now, finally, she was at rest from the tormenting devils in her mind.

Depression Hits Alexandria

The year is 1931

In London, Oswald Mosley forms the New Party, dedicated to Parliamentary Reform.

In Germany, after the collapse of the Danatbank and the closure of all banks, Britain, the USA and France renew recent credits for Germany for three months to help them through their financial difficulties.

In Spain, King Alfonso XIII abdicates and is forced to flee the country.

In Rome, the Pope denounces Mussolini's Fascists, following attacks on priests and church property.

Meanwhile, in the far-flung world of Egypt, all was not well in the Petropoulos household. Georgos was now undergoing severe financial troubles. He had ventured into the real estate business. He borrowed money to buy land to build villas and apartments, which were, in fact, luxury habitations, and then when completed, would be sold at a very handsome profit.

This scheme went on quite well for a long time. He was an outstanding architect with an excellent reputation; a hard worker who did not cut corners on materials. Only the best materials were used, which in turn acquired many satisfied customers.

Alexandria was on the brink of bankruptcy. The banks were foreclosing, and depression was now lying across his very own doorstep. The houses and villas Georgos had built, so beautiful and luxurious, were now lying empty and unsaleable. Buyers were cautious and stayed away, yet the loans from the banks had to be met. He who had succeeded brilliantly as an architect, building beautiful homes for sale, was now desperately trying to negotiate with the banks, pleading for more time. The banks threatened to repossess all the new homes, and their refusal to extend their credit meant a cataclysmic cycle of events that would mean sheer ruin for him and his family.

In desperation, Georgos turned now to the Freemasons. Being a fellow member for many, many years, he had often been instrumental in giving a helping hand to others who were experiencing hardship. The only 'provisor' being that the source of the gift of either money or a helping hand would never be disclosed to anyone. Such were the rules of the Freemasons.

Overcoming his 'filotimo' (dignity), which was ever so profoundly engrained in many Greeks, he sought help from those who wielded influence in the high echelons of business and had been fellow members in the secretive society of the Freemasons.

They turned him down. The society he had belonged to was unable to help Georgos now in this time of severe depression. His run of luck had ended now. He had staked his last card. Now he knew for certain that the banks would strip him of each and every house that he had so lovingly prepared. All this hard work, effort and money he had deployed would all be lost. The dowry he had provided for Erietta to enter into a good marriage would now be eradicated in the repayment of monies to the banks.

The hand of God was not on his shoulder. His spirits were gone, and all the fears that had been in his heart since the depression started were now confirmed. The future was dark and threatening. Like the broken branches of a fallen tree, his spirit withered and died, alongside all the hopes and dreams that he had for his children, Damy and Erietta.

But for now, Georgos put all the world's worries firmly aside. It was time for the hammer to hit the nail! At stake now was his daughter's fate and happiness. Her intended suitor was this very afternoon coming to visit their home accompanied by the ever-respectable Mrs Georgiades, the marriage arranger. Could and would this Greek man, the said

Panayotis Meletis, find in Erietta the perfect wife he was seeking? As a father, his heart was breaking at the thought of losing his beloved Erietta, for his only son, Damy, was still in Austria in the final stages of studying to be an architect.

His head now ruled his heart, and in the deep recesses of his mind, he knew that the marriage would solve one of his many problems—someone who would take care of Erietta when his financial world would come crashing down around him.

It was now four o'clock. Outside, the stark naked blazing Egyptian sun gave way to the breezy afternoon. From the top floor of the Petropoulos family home, noisy shutters were being flung open. Maria rose from her siesta and was more than ready to put the final touches to playing hostess to Mrs Georgiades and the young man she was bringing with her. For Erietta now, the minutes were ticking by; the silence of the siesta hour was shattered by the beautiful sound of the grandfather clock, which stood majestically in the 'saloni'— the family's living room.

Slowly now, Erietta came down the beautiful cloisonné sculptured staircase and stepped onto the black and white marbled floor before entering the saloni. Silently, she stopped, and pirouetting first on one foot, then on another, tried to visualise how her family home would appear to this stranger they were welcoming that very day. Her eyes darted to the crystal chandeliers, which dominated the entire saloni. Then her sights took in the kaleidoscope of her mind's eye to the grand piano that held pride of place within the room.

Earlier in the day, Maria had told Erietta that she had something to discuss with her. The time had come for Erietta to know the truth. Maria looked up from the petit point needlework on her lap as Erietta entered the saloni and sat down. Putting the needlework aside, she wondered not for the first time, how she would break the news to her headstrong step-daughter.

"Erietta," she began. "I am not going to prevaricate; I shall come straight to the point with clarity and honesty."

Erietta felt her heart sink with apprehension. These were ominous words, words that struck terror like a horror movie, evil and fowl. She could almost taste the bitter bile that arose from way down her soul. Outwardly calm and cool, she stared straight ahead, sitting upright. She was certainly not giving Maria the satisfaction of being at all perturbed, she thought. Such was the game that each played silently, like two gladiators, eyeing and assessing strengths and weaknesses.

Maria continued in a low tone, "Your father is bankrupt. There is no money left! The houses he has built up and worked for are lying idle, with no buyers forthcoming. The banks are foreclosing on him. Everything is going; we will lose this house too."

During the ensuing silence, Maria sat and observed Erietta, who was desperately trying to comprehend what had just been said. Her face was etched with misery, no pretence left as she desperately sought Maria's eyes as if to ascertain if it was a huge joke, a mistake perhaps. Maria stared back, unsmiling and unwavering. Thus a silent confirmation flowed through to Erietta. No joke. No mistake. No turning away from reality. She could read it all in Maria's face.

"And as you know," continued Maria relentlessly, "The dowry that was set aside for you was loaned to your brother Damy to complete his studies abroad."

Erietta bowed her head. Yes, she remembered, for it was with her utter and complete consent that the money put aside for her by her father to enable her to enter into a good marriage had been loaned to Damy to complete his architecttural studies in Austria.

"Don't look so worried," continued Maria. "You are only twenty-six. You have all the time in the world to start again."

Erietta looked at her and attempted a smile. For once, they were united in a cause that bound them together. The distress would be so great that it was about to change their whole existence. There were no tomorrows left for planning, just a dusty cloud of uncertainty setting in.

"You keep telling me I'm young, but at the moment, I feel old and tired and jaded. A thousand questions are going round and round in my head. Where will we go? What will happen to us?"

"Your father and I talked well into the night for weeks now," continued Maria. She felt truly sorry for Erietta, who had already suffered the loss of a mother at such an early age, for she was just six years old at the time. She knew she must have missed the tender love of her mother.

Diamandis (Damy) Petropoulos

Damy as a student aged 14 in Alexandria in 1917.

Damy remembered how as children, he and Erietta were not allowed to bring any friends home and the many times they had been disciplined by their father when they had slightly upset Maria in any way. They were not allowed to play the piano, which stood silent under lock and key. The shutters had to remain closed, as, in Maria's opinion, sunshine filtering in would fade the furnishing indoors. Maria was suffering more and more from depression and bouts of ill-health. Whilst Maria took herself to bed, Erietta took care of the household, the servants and her father's well-being.

Damy left Alexandria for Austria, where a place awaited him in cram school to learn the language and start university life.

From an early age, he had made up his mind to get out of the household that he and Erietta had suffered at. The best way to do so was to study hard and achieve the grades which would enable him to become an architect just like his father. It had taken Damy ten years to become a fully-fledged architect.

He had settled quite well into his university life and made many, many friends, most being of the fairer sex. By all accounts, he was handsome and a terrific flirt, and during the ten years, he had broken quite a few hearts.

He loved Austria. The scenery and the people were like a heady wine that went to his head. He was taken everywhere, wined and dined, and had the time of his life. During the latter part of his second year, he had even acquired a mistress, a lovely German girl, fair-haired, tall and intelligent, though a few years older than Damy.

It was Eva who persuaded him to write to his father and ask him to give his acquiescence to Damy taking a sabbatical, a year off from his studies, to get around and see life before he finally acquired his degree and settled down for married life and its responsibilities. He strongly felt now was the time to enjoy his life, that such an opportunity might never present itself again.

The reply that came back was swift, strong and final. No studies meant no money was to be forwarded to him. The simple truth was that Georgos was bankrupt! The only money left was Erietta's dowry money, and that was an honourable commitment that Georgos had made to his daughter while he had sent Damy to Austria. In no way was that dowry to be touched or used as security. Quite simple, though quite unexpected, to Damy, who had different visions of his father's understanding. He felt cheated and misunderstood. How could a year taken off his studies matter? All too soon, he would be encumbered with duties and life.

Damy then made a promise. If his father were to loan him Erietta's dowry, the loan would be repaid as soon as he graduated. He would consider it as a debt of honour.

Erietta, who had always been very close to Damy, wished that the money be sent to him, thus enabling him to finish his studies. So, the money that would have secured Erietta, perhaps with a comfortable marriage, was sent on to

Damy, and true to his word, he graduated as an architect with honours, much to the delight and pride of Georgos.

He decided he would stay on in Graz and pay his own way. He felt that would not be such a problem. He was young, good looking and spoke fluent German—a bright spark. Every employer's dream of an employee. A temporary measure, nevertheless. He knew in his heart of hearts that he wanted and desired to use his degree.

Damy in Austria aged 20.

His search for a job, any job, was not as easy as he had first imagined. Whilst he could and did have lodgings with Eva, and the question of him paying for his own food never arose, there remained a small matter of spending money which up to now had been a generous allowance from Alexandria.

Damy had spent many a lovely afternoon and evening at the Palaces de Thés Dansant and Soirées Dansant. These were places where the music was by an excellent band, where you could spend a few hours sipping tea and find a partner to dance with. These were respectful establishments and had further acquired a good reputation for people of genteel background to spend an evening. For the price of a few pfennigs, you bought a series of tickets, which enabled you to go up to the 'hired partner' that would either be a man or a woman.

Having returned home to Alexandria, it soon became apparent that there was no money to be made as an architect. Alas, the streets of Alexandria were not paved with gold. Damy was impatient. He wanted to make his mark quickly. He felt he had wasted enough precious time. He knew in his heart of hearts that Alexandria would not and could not offer him all that time he had worked and studied hard for.

He now turned his attention to Greece. Every Greek living abroad and away from Greece thinks of themselves as being "xenitia" (a foreigner), though their hearts will always remain anchored in their home country.

Once more, Damy set forth from Alexandria, leaving behind his family to seek home and fortune in his 'patrída'—his home country—Greece.

For the second time, Erietta was losing her brother. Her father was bankrupt. Her future looked bleak. Furthermore, with no dowry, no well-to-do Greek with prospects would come like a knight in shining armour and rescue her from the plight and downfall the Petropoulos family were at present experiencing.

This very morning, Maria had informed her of the dire state of her father's affairs, whilst at the same time, acquainting her of the fact that Mrs Georgiades had found a suitable prospect for Erietta.

How could she? How could anyone spend the rest of their lives with someone they had never met, never seen, knew nothing about, build a life with, and have a family with?

What if she did not like his looks? What if he was old? What if he was fat, ill-mannered, uncouth, dirty, smelly, a drinker, a gambler?

Stop, she told herself, *let reason prevail.*

What were her options?

None. Her father was bankrupt. With little or no money, the household would be a breeding ground for Maria's endless depressions—a virtual living death. That part of her life had to end. It was a one-way street. No u-turns allowed!

The Son of Sirens

As the hours ticked by, Erietta became aware that the moment had come when she would meet her 'fate'. Mrs Georgiades, the time-honoured and well-respected marriage arranger, would be paying a visit this very day, and bringing with her, Erietta's possible future husband.

Mira, one of the Greek Fates, had produced a joker in the form of a marriage matchmaker. This was the one card Erietta could not discard. The choices were now non-existent. She was a realist, and realists know the moment they have entered the dead-end street of life.

In accordance with Greek traditions at the time, arranged marriages were the best.

She wandered now into the kitchen with its marble floor and pristine white cupboards, and her steps took her into the library, with its tall windows and shutters, with books lying from floor to ceiling. This was the room that she loved above all. Every corner, every book on the shelves in front of her held a fond memory of the many hours she had spent escaping the outside world.

The thought of her turning her back to this, her beloved home, made her feel inconsolably sad and tearful. She tried to tell herself that it was only, after all, a house. Only bricks on bricks held together with cement. Just rooms with walls and floors. But this had been her whole world from the time her mother lived there, before her death. She felt she belonged to it, as much as the house belonged to her.

Erietta sighed now. There was no escape! A husband it had to be. After all, what were her alternatives? She was, after all, a prisoner of her time and the society she grew up in. Women of her class did not work, although of course some did, and depressing work it was, too. She, for once, had no intention whatsoever of dwindling away her days as some governess or even someone's companion. She had been that throughout her childhood, and right through her teenage years to Maria, her stepmother.

She calmly thought of the prospective bridegroom, this Panayotis Meletis, and cheerfully acknowledged the fact that he too knew nothing, absolutely nothing about her. *Serves him right!* she thought.

She now weighed all her options, reason once more prevailed, and she looked forward to meeting her prospective husband with anticipation and a sense of adventure.

What else? All her boats had been burnt behind her.

Panayotis Meletis was her future, her hope, her escape, and her chance to live again and build something with her life.

And who knows, maybe, just maybe, she might learn to love him, this unknown stranger.

Her acquiescence now to the forthcoming marriage arrangement had a strong tide of pure resentment. She would do as they wanted her to and marry, but only because there was no alternative. She was frightened by the feeling that there was no escape from the hard and cruel choices that life bestowed randomly! Her friends had reminded her often of the saying that *"Greeks may soar but keep their feet well on the ground."*

Meanwhile, back in the Petropoulos household, Mrs Georgiades had arrived and been ushered into the drawing room, with Panayotis at her side.

After the obligatory introductions were made, Erietta stole a glance at Panayotis and invited him to take a stroll into the garden, but before she could stop herself, she told him that he was just someone that was going to rescue her from the wretched state of spinsterhood, and also from her father's untimely end of his business and his livelihood.

Her chin was now held high in defiance, and her green eyes flashed with a temper that had been looming inside like a runaway train for many days. The outcome was a tirade that lashed out of control.

She took a step forward and proceeded to tell him that she was not free, for she had to carry out her father's wishes, obey his commands and at this moment in time, marriage was the last thing she wanted, for, in her mind's eye, this was not going to be a heart-thumping approach with a touch of romantic illusion at its core, such of which only dreams were made of.

Deep inside, she was a little apprehensive about her outburst, but she pushed her fear aside for the moment. It was time someone listened to what she had to say! It was just Panayotis' bad luck that he happened to be here now when everything erupted inside her. She now stopped and waited. Panayotis stood perfectly still with his eyes closed now. Not a muscle moved. Finally, looking straight at Erietta, he said in a quiet tone, "We actually begin luckier than some as we have no illusions. We could be very good friends. That is all I want now. I need a partner to go with me through the treadmill of life. I need someone who will enhance my social standing. There is a dynamo inside of me that my parents always insisted had been there since I was born. I fully intend to make inroads and establish myself in the business world! For this reason, I have studied and sat many exams, the outcome being that I am now a fully qualified Chartered Accountant."

"Fine!" was all she said, and they looked at each other. There was no emotion, no romance, no sentiment, no illusions, no love lost between the two would-be partners for life. They were building a lifetime on less than nothing!

The next afternoon, a telegram arrived addressed to Erietta, which simply stated, "I too am nervous!" signed Noti. That was the nickname Panayotis was known by.

His deep understanding of her feelings swayed Erietta. He was for her now the Son of Sirens—her fate.

Erietta and Noti

A Summer Wedding

Winter had fled, taking with it the bare trees, bereft of leaves, the dark nights and the flowerless gardens. For now, it was the turn of spring.

Despite its woes, uncertainty, injustices and pain, the world continued its cycle of seasons, as it had done for many, many thousands of years.

The distance of time, endured day in and day out, year after year, aeon after aeon, unfailing, unchanged and with such fixity of purpose could only be the work of a higher being—a God. The work of a father whose children need permanency, where you simply had to look at nature of experience, the momentum of faith!

For now, summer in all its glory had arrived. All around, the bare arms of trees were fully rigged in their best attire of glossy, cascading leaves of different hues of green. Beautiful buds and blossoms adorned every flower, and at night the heavenly smell of jasmine and mimosa pervaded the streets. The early dawn chorus of the birds and the hazy mornings that brought a promise of sunshine and light, all heralded the birth of summer.

Arrangements for a summer wedding between Panayotis Meletis and Erietta Petropoulos were going ahead as planned. It was going to be a simple affair, due to the money situation, or more precisely the lack of it!

It was a great tradition that an accepted 'courtship' took place as soon as matters were settled between the bride's father and the future husband. There were things to be discussed, projects to be planned, ideas to be exchanged and an in-depth search of each other's character was to take place. This was indeed important, essential in fact, in getting to know the stranger you were going to spend the rest of your life with, as Erietta was about to.

Noti had been offered a position as a Chief Accountant, leading to a partnership in time with a firm of considerable reputation. Lindi was a large firm of wholesale importers of luxury goods from faraway places. From champagne and cognac to fine wines from the eclectic vineyards of France to the mouth-watering Italian hams, cheese, Portugese sherry and wines, and Russian caviar—the finest such as Beluga. Scotland and its distilleries provided the best whiskies, and Austria provided venison and pheasants, which adorned the Christmas tables. All sorts of luxury tinned provisions, such as chestnuts in liquor and much, much more, were also provided. All such victuals were sought after by big hotels in Cairo, such as The Shepherds, Mena House and

Semiramis, whose customers demanded and expected the best of everything their money could buy.

Occasionally too, a call would come from Abdine Palace, the summer residence of King Farouk of Egypt and his first wife Queen Farida, meaning 'the flawless one'. They would order some item or other of utter delectation, and when this happened, the firm of Lindi was ecstatic.

Noti in the conference room with his employees, which took place once a month.

Noti exhibiting some of the products that his company, Lindi produced.

There was just one tiny flaw. The firm was based in Cairo, and if Noti accepted the position, he and Erietta would have to leave behind Alexandria, their parents, their friends and their way of life and settle in a new city.

Just like Ruth in the story of the Bible, Erietta was ready to create a new life in Cairo with Noti, with absolutely no hesitation. 'New Beginnings', she called it.

Now the boy from Smyrna, the beloved city that Alexander the Great had built, was to be joined in marriage to Erietta, who had lived in Alexandria, the city Alexander the Great had conquered and named after himself in 332 B.C. Was that merely a coincidence or an omen for the young couple?

Mira

Two weeks before the wedding was to occur, the Fates, or Mira as they were known in Greek mythology, where the three daughters of Zeus, who spun the web of life, measured it, then cut it out and distributed it accordingly, struck a blow, and threw a spanner in the midst of the marriage preparations that were to take place.

For now, the impending foreclosure of the banks on money owed by Georgos for his unsold empty luxury homes came sooner than he expected. Thus, the dowry promised by Erietta's father to set up Noti was now null and void.

The cupboard in the Petropoulos household was bare. The coffers empty. All funds had sunk. Even the mice had gone away of their own accord.

Under the circumstances, it would have been acceptable, indeed quite understandable, if Noti had withdrawn from the marriage agreement. Indeed, all of Erietta's family and friends quite expected him to. Erietta was inconsolable, distraught, her mind petrified. Her thoughts were in a fierce frenzy, rolling aimlessly and without sequence.

All her hopes, plans, dreams and thoughts were now beyond reach. The blueprint of her life was to be destroyed.

Goodbye hope—abandon all expectations. Every aspiration and dreams she ever had were now a castle in the air. The bottom of Pandora's box had now, at this moment in time, been reached.

After a week of utter silence, with no communication whatsoever forthcoming, Noti arrived late one night at the Petropoulos household, and without much ado, informed the whole family that the dowry, or the lack of it, made no difference. Nevertheless, the wedding was to go ahead in Alexandria as planned for 11th July 1931.

Erietta now came to realise that Noti's immense strength lay in his steadfastness and his ability to plod on, regardless, once his mind was made up.

Goodbye Alexandria

It was time! The train now at Alexandria Station stood by on Platform 12, restlessly oscillating its powerful engine, ready to take off. On the platform stood Noti and Erietta, their bags packed and ready to board the train to take them from Alexandria to their new life together in Cairo.

Their parents, friends and neighbours, who had come to see them off, surrounded them. Many of them knew full well that this might be the last time they saw each other. The laughter that had predominated the group of people who had arrived to see them off now turned to tears, as fond farewells, embraces, hugs and kisses from all sides transformed their departure into a melancholic occurrence.

The strident sound from the station masters' whistle, a burst of hiss from the steam engine and the vociferous shout of "all aboard" heralded the cutting of the Gordion Knot for all those who had gathered there.

Although the thought of losing Erietta broke his heart, Georgos knew, without a shadow of a doubt, that Noti was quite capable of looking after her, and that was consolation enough for him.

As they took their seats by the window, Erietta now leaned right out of the departing train, witnessing like a silent movie, those piteous friends getting smaller and smaller as the train gathered momentum, but still waving their tiny handkerchiefs all the while. It was a heart-breaking sight. Impetuously now, she felt the urge to stop the train and run back to the life she was leaving behind.

With an unexpected burst like a thunderclap, the window suddenly came down. Noti sat down again. Erietta, taken by surprise, dropped from the clouds, unaware and unsure of Noti's intentions. "Do not look back," he said, "for now is the time to look to the future in front of us. There is no need to watch the bridges that are burning, for a new life, a new adventure awaits us," Noti told her.

Slowly, her features regained their tranquillity of thoughts; the sad shadows visible beyond her eyes slowly disappeared. Her new world was waiting. It was, at present, all down to her, for at this juncture, she and only she was in charge of her destiny. The challenge was hers to take.

The sight of a 'sakieh' (a water wheel), driven by the sheer power of a yoked ox who, blindfolded, endlessly went round and round, caught Erietta's eye now. Vast stretches of desert appeared now, and from time to time, so did camels, the traditional ships of the desert, as they are known. Gawky, haughty silly-looking beasts stood together around an oasis in the shade of a few date palm trees, their eyes menacing all the while, standing on their huge padded feet, resting before their long trek through the desert.

Slowly now, the train came to a halt at Cairo station. They had arrived. As they descended from their enclosed carriage into the world beyond, Erietta and Noti were overwhelmed by the noise. Everybody tried to shout above the din and cacophony around them in order to be heard. Here and there came loud shrieks of laughter as pedestrians jostled between the cars, taxis, bicycles, and handcarts. Horns honked, while loud music blared from every corner. Cycle belts rang continually, and every few miles, a traffic policeman gallantly fought a losing battle with his staccato burst of whistles. It was a no-win state of sheer defiance.

Trying to get a taxi to take them to their new home, both Erietta and Noti witnessed the craziest traffic in the world!

They found a flat in the select district of Heliopolis—City of the Sun. The fourth floor housed an enormous veranda that would give way to a cool afternoon after the siesta hour when the sun shone brightly. The open-air veranda held a table, chairs and settees, and at night, friends and neighbours would gather around to enjoy each other's company, with each person bringing food to save the hostess from cooking. One neighbour would even bring a mandolin or an accordion to provide music for the evening. The views were spectacular and being so high up meant the stars shone down like scintillating diamonds across the sky.

They were happy and settled in their new home. Noti and Erietta were overjoyed when on 23rd July 1932, a little girl was born, whom they named Angela, after Noti's mother, as was the custom. This little girl would grow into a headstrong, determined woman.

This little girl is also the person who has written this book.

Fast forward now to the day of 1st April 1938. Noti took Erietta to the hospital, where she was to give birth for the second time.

The following day, on 2nd April, Noti phoned to find out the gender of the baby—only to be told to his utter disbelief that not only were the newborns twins, but they were both girls. Quite laughingly now, he replied, "Joke over, April Fools' Day has been and gone yesterday." They named their girls Fanoula (Fani) and Maria (Mitzi) in line with family tradition. The children had a good life and completed the

Meletis family. Noti and Erietta had many beautiful years together, raising their family of five.

Erietta and Noti with their three children, Angela, Maria and Fanoula, with the servant's daughter in the background.

Noti

Panayotis Meletis

Panayotis 'Noti' Meletis was born in Karatas in Smyrna, Turkey, on 15th December 1907.

His father was Alexandros, and his mother, Anghela. They had a daughter born two years after Noti's birth, but sadly for both of them, she died when only a few months old.

Alexandros and Anghela were truly heartbroken. They both loved children and now knew they could not have any more.

We now know Alexandros' father was called Zaharias, as to his wife's name—we know not!

So many roots erased and lost, like so many stitches that have been dropped and never picked up in the final finished pattern of life. Such a deep sense of loss to those now great-grandchildren, and such a shame and waste too.

If only one paid more attention when a name is fleetingly spoken by parents and grandparents. If only at the given time of growing up, enough importance is placed on those names of people who once formed the family knot and have since been erased forever from the blackboard of life.

Regrets occur many generations later. By then, too late, the time has erased not only every tiny speck of memory, but those that knew and could have told us have long since departed.

To the shame of those future generations, no trace remains—no footprints have been left behind to follow through.

Like many Greek marriages, this was an arranged marriage for both Alexandros and Anghela and a very happy one, too.

Indeed, Alexandros considered himself a very lucky man and had grown to love Anghela over the years, deeply.

Anghela was small, very slightly built, with a youth's figure. She had an abundance of chestnut hair which she wore like a halo around her face in plaits. She could not be called pretty in the conventional sense of the word, but she had beautiful brown eyes that shone with joy and a smile that often turned into laughter and made her a very attractive girl indeed.

Their characters surprisingly were in stark contrast as well. Alexandros was placid and easy-going, whereas Anghela was impatient. He was content to sit around the home quietly contemplating life until the next job came along. Anghela, on the other hand, was possessed with a tremendous zest for life and a great sense of adventure.

Alexandros was an engineer, and thus the family was relatively comfortable. He would be in charge of setting up a farm, for instance. That meant that he had to see and participate in the erection of the gas mains (no electricity in those days), the sanitation and pipework, as well as many other engineering feats.

His work often took him around many districts, and sometimes he would be gone for many days, which could also turn into weeks and months.

When his work finished, Alexandros would then return home laden with chickens, ham, eggs and vegetables. A veritable feast indeed, and one that would be shared with all their nearby neighbours and friends, for this was a very closely-knit community.

In times of need, illness and sorrow, friends and neighbours were there seeing to everything. If someone was dying, everyone would take turns sitting next to the person who was very ill, never leaving them on their own.

Whether awake or asleep, there would always be someone to hold their hand, to whisper to, to ease their way into the other world—never alone!

Upon Alexandros' return and after having seen to the family's needs and necessities, he would store a few coins safely amongst the clothes in the 'Baoulo'— that very Greek trunk that had once stored Anghela's dowry of clothes, bed linen, towels etc. The trunk was now used to store the winter clothes and the knitted garments which were kept amongst a lot of 'Nafthalini' (mothballs), to keep the moths at bay.

Greek husbands trusted their wives better than they trusted the banks, so their money was stored safely away in either the Baoulo or inside a mattress for safekeeping until needed.

Little did Alexandros know then that this simple gesture would mean the difference between living and dying— deaths so horrendous, so atrocious, that nations would weep.

Thousands of Greeks would be destroyed, burnt and raped, and many more would be scattered across the world to countries beyond, seeking refuge.

Those then would be lucky ones, the ones that had some money—money that would buy them their life ticket to safety.

In Smyrna, at the time when Noti was growing up, the hubbub of all Greek life was the local 'Kafenion'—that coffee place. It was the meeting place for music lovers, retired lawyers, schoolteachers, farmers, poets, and gossip lovers.

The local kafenions were for members of any class, profession or persuasion. The average citizen would find the best source of news, gossip, rumour, or sometimes the orchestration of the ruination of a character or two there.

Over a sip of Ouzo or a cup of Greek coffee, they would sit all day either playing 'Tavli' (backgammon) or smoking 'Nargiles' (hookah pipe) for a spot of relaxation, and that favourite pastime of the Greeks—discussing and arguing about everything from the all-important politics (the Greeks take their politics very seriously indeed) to the price of oil.

The locals would recount stories about dangerous deep-sea fishing and sponge diving, stories of yesteryear. The focal point was the mandolin players who would make up and sing the stories of the day's events through their 'mantinades' verses sung to the tunes of popular songs.

How Anghela longed to sit amongst the locals in the Kafenion listening to the elders reminiscing about the old life in the village, while smelling the special Kafenion smells which were awash with the aroma of the coffee, incense and pungent spices.

The fact that she was a woman and that the Kafenion was largely a male enclave didn't stop her, as she laughingly recounted later to her grandchildren.

With a great sense of adventure, coupled with trepidation, she would dress in men's clothes, gather her hair up in a man's hat and, being of small build, pass for a young lad.

Sitting quietly and inconspicuously, she would listen avidly to the locals, whose conversation would turn to memories of places they had once visited. They spoke of the village tradesman, the potter, the carpenter, the sandal maker and shoemaker, the basket and cloth weavers, the butcher, the baker and the candlestick-maker.

Anghela was truly a woman of tomorrow, born in a very traditional past, and this was indeed, for her time, an avant-garde stance to take.

She had no need of chaining herself to railings, haranguing about women's rights and freedom. Quietly and surreptitiously, cunningly and stealthily, she infiltrated the men's domain and with the use of sign language to the waiter, managed a few hours of clandestine adventure.

From the cradle to the grave, women have always found ways of getting their own way stealthily.

They use their so-called 'weakness' as a weapon to get their way through tears and sighs, and the very Greek 'krevato murmura' meaning 'bed moans'; the ultimate weapon which is guaranteed never to fail. You wait until the man is just about to go to sleep, all relaxed, then you start your string of complaints!

On the other hand, Anghela was a loving wife, an exceptional housewife and the best of mothers. Her hand-knitted garments were the talk of the neighbourhood; from pullovers to socks, her nimble fingers never seemed to stop.

Like Fani in the story of Erietta, she was a great believer in the foretelling of fortunes by way of Tarot cards and also of the 'Flitzani'—that traditional Greek ceremony of coffee drinking that women gather for, where the sediments left in the bottom of the cup are interpreted by the Flitzanou, the coffee fortune teller.

Anghela would often gather with her friends and laughingly spend mornings together, having their fortunes told.

Smyrna—The City with a Dramatic Past

Meanwhile, across the shores of Greece, the Greeks had elected a president called Eleftherios Venizelos. He was a man of vision and a crusader of lost causes. Not just that but a man, alas, whose subsequent actions were to become the very instrument that brought about the change in the whole structure of Asia Minor and the collapse and obliteration of the Christian civilisation of Smyrna in its wake.

Venizelos was fired by a passionate belief that there would be a time when every Greek man, woman and child living in and around Smyrna and Constantinople, in Asia Minor, would no longer have to live under the yoke of their Turkish masters. He believed that they should be able to go about their daily lives as free people with dignity and freedom once more restored to them—those very sacred rights that had been stripped away by decades of enslavement.

Thus, consumed by a fervour that knew no bounds, he presented the case of the Greeks living in Asia Minor at the Versailles Peace talks with such eloquence that he was given the go-ahead by the Allies to free Smyrna and Constantinople and bring about once more under Greek rule the vast Turkish areas that had once long ago been part of the Byzantine Empire.

Now it was the turn of the Greek army to round up the Turks, civilians and soldiers, killing and wounding many. They were, in fact, merely repaying the Turks for the suffering and abject slavery that their forefathers had endured for so long. However, the attainment of their vision and the fulfilment of their dreams were still as far removed as the moon is from the earth.

Then followed the defeat of the Turkish army by the Greek army. Thus, having tasted the sweet taste of victory, the Greek army decided to invade Turkey and penetrated the mainland with the help of the then Greek population. This is known throughout history as the Greco-Turkish War (1897).

The morale of the now beaten Turkish army was at its lowest. The hitherto unexpected had happened; they had been beaten by none other than the mere Greeks, and it seemed that they had no desire left with which to fight back. The story does not simply end here. What happened after this victory many years later played an important part in the life story of Noti. This will be revealed as the pages unfold.

Life with the Meletis Family

Alexandros Meletis sat surrounded by plans, sketches and drawings. Another job loomed ahead that required his engineering skills, time and planning in the setting up of a present derelict stretch of land that a Turkish family wanted to convert in the near future to a cotton-producing farm.

As the father had recently died after a prolonged and wasteful time in bed with Tuberculosis, the land was now passed on to the one and only son, Suliman, who had many options to take into consideration.

This fair-sized bit of land to the north of Constantinople could, if sold, fetch a very handsome price, bearing in mind that the soil was exceptionally good. It could easily be turned into an agricultural farm, producing crops that would grow easily, or a tobacco farm that would yield good quality plants for grade one tobacco, or indeed as the present heir and owner were contemplating, a good cotton enterprise.

Alexandros was now busy submitting plans and drawings for all the engineering feats that his expertise was going to have to deal with. The laying of drainage, gas piping and much more would transform the farm into a working unit. Architects had been called to submit drawings for a home to be built—a home that the Turkish family would live and work from.

From the back garden came the sounds of the few chickens that were squawkingly settling down for the night in the 'Kotetsi' (the chicken coop). Alexandros smiled, remembering the time all those years ago when he and Anghela, his beloved wife, had decided to build a small kotetsi, not too large, but large enough for Noti, who was a toddler back then, to have fresh eggs every day. Over the years, many more eggs had hatched, and many chicks had been born. From the early age of six, Noti had taken over the looking after of the 'Kotes' (the chickens). As they produced new chicks, he would lovingly look after them, keep them warm for the crucial first days, feed them and when ready, he would sell them at the open market 'Ahora', which was held once a week in Smyrna.

All the farmers would come from neighbouring areas to display and sell their vegetables and fruits. The village women came along too to display their embroidery and crochet work they had been busily working on throughout the cold dark winter nights, to which they hoped to sell. Chickens, pigs, sweetly singing yellow canaries in cages, brooms, pots, pans, cutlery and glasses, along with small coffee cups with the many varying sizes of the most important utensil in the Greek household, the 'Briki' which produced the thick sediment-laden, strong Greek coffee, were also sold.

Apart from the raising of chicks and the selling thereof, Noti successfully raised rabbits that fetched good prices. He sold these rabbits to the local butcher, who in turn supplied the whole neighbourhood.

Both Anghela and Alexandros firmly believed that earned money held a much higher value to the growing boy and a greater appreciation of what hard work meant in the long run. Therefore, both of them encouraged and praised Noti in his endeavours.

The money earned went towards books, birthday presents, Christmas presents and much more besides.

But saving up meant much more to Noti than the purchase of goods. It meant the fulfilment of his dream, a dream that had been with him since he had been a youngster, knee-high. He did not know how or when this came about, but his burning ambition was to train and one day become a surgeon, and every coin saved meant that he would have enough to see him through his training.

His mother and father, although wishing him to progress in life, tried to point out the pitfalls, hard work, dedication and training that he would have to undergo to fulfil his ambition. They tried to point out that whilst his friends would be safely and securely earning good money in some other profession, married with a family, Noti would have to sacrifice for years to study in relative poverty.

Baby Ahmed

A year and a half had gone by since Alexandros had been installing with his workmen the drainage and pipework of the land that the Turkish family owned. The land was to be turned into a tobacco plantation in time for the present owner's return from serving his military service away.

On the farmhouse lived the mother and father of the young soldier Suliman, together with his wife, Zeinab, and their baby, Ahmed. They all lived in close harmony; both women looked after all the jobs around the farm, the chickens, the cows and the milking, while the men tended to the fields under the supervision of the grandfather.

Work was hard, but the family united together and pulled along, waiting for the time when Suliman would finish his military service and join them in the running of the tobacco plantation venture. Work was progressing satisfactorily; Alexandros was quite pleased.

On the two occasions that the young soldier had come home on leave to see his family, he too seemed happy with the progress.

One night, one of the workers came to call on Suliman's wife, asking for the medicine man to be sent for. His wife was struggling to breathe and was burning with fever. Quickly, Zeinab went to the man's home to see if she could be of any help whilst waiting for the medicine man to arrive, for the roads then were bad, and the distances great.

That gesture of kindness was a mistake—a mistake that would cost Zeinab her life, leaving behind a small baby as an orphan. The disease was diagnosed as Diphtheria, which happened to be contagious too. Within a week, Zeinab had contracted the disease herself, and a few hours later, she died. There was nothing anyone could do apart from keeping the baby away for fear of him contracting the disease too.

After the usual quarantine was up, life did not settle into the usual pattern as before. The grandmother fell into an endless pit of depression, being of no help to anyone, neither to her grandson nor to the household.

The grandfather, having gone through a period of mourning, knew that it was up to him to sort all the problems out. He accepted the fact that his wife could no longer look after the baby and that he himself would be busy as ever before, supervising the workmen and looking after the farm. The child could not remain and be looked after properly by the servants. He knew that his son, if he were here, would not deem this to be an acceptable long-term solution for Ahmed.

Alexandros stepped in, and in view of the fact that his work had now ended, he proposed to the grandfather that his family could look after Ahmed until his father was discharged from his military service and was able to find a better solution.

Over the months that Alexandros had been with the family busily turning the land into a tobacco plantation with all its requisites, the grandfather had come to know and respect Alexandros, not only for his professional expertise but also for the fact that Alexandros himself was a family man who deeply loved his wife and son and spoke endlessly about them with pride and love. Thus, the grandfather accepted the temporary solution, albeit with a heavy heart.

Not once did Alexandros stop to think that Anghela would not welcome the baby or that perhaps she may find that it entailed a lot more work for her. He knew her to be a kind-hearted woman with an abundance of love to give. Noti, now grown up, did not need her as much.

The decision taken, Alexandros returned to Karatas, his home, with baby Ahmed by his side. As he had expected, the boy settled down with his new family quite well. He was a loving youngster, full of mischief and full of giving. Noti became his hero, showing him how to fish and feed and look after the chickens, and soon he became a loving part of the family.

A year and a half had gone by and baby Ahmed was now two years old and happily ensconced in the Meletis household. So much so that everyone had almost forgotten that the day would eventually come when he would have to leave them forever.

Alexandros would tell Anghela over and over again not to get too attached to Ahmed, for he was only on loan, but she would laugh and chase him away. It truly saddened him to see her acting as if she was the natural mother, caring for the boy over and above any sense of duty.

Well, the time had come now—Ahmed's father would scoop him up and away from them when the morning chased the night away. This time tomorrow, there would be nothing to show that the youngster had been with them for over a year. Only the deep silence echoing in the room with an empty cot would greet Anghela when she first woke up.

Destiny could no longer be forestalled. The dice were cast. Not one person had the right or power to change tomorrow's event.

The Messenger

Silently and reluctantly, Alexandros took the few steps that separated the drawing room and the neglected work in his study into the kitchen where Anghela was baking. The kitchen was where everyone liked to be, with all the lovely smells pervading all day long.

Now at the end of the summer, Anghela was busy every day. Jam making was in full process. Date jam was being made from fresh black dates which had been peeled and the stone removed and stuffed in its place with pinecone seeds. There would be rose jam, deliciously made with the petals of the roses, together with walnuts. Orange jam, quince jam and much more would be brought out on the breakfast table in the winter mornings.

It was the time of the year when the jam-making smells would linger and linger in and around the kitchen for days on end.

The sun was setting slowly now, and Alexandros stood idly watching the sky in all its beauty from the doors that led from his study into the beautiful front garden. The flowers were a kaleidoscope of brightness, as this summer, nature had produced a riot of colours. The bees were busily darting in and out through the heart of every brightly coloured flower.

The shadows cast by the dying summer sun were reflected on the garden's sundial and the birdbath enjoyed the company of a few sparrows swooping in and out, splashing little droplets of water around them.

Soon Anghela would be out there setting the table with a crisp tablecloth and a freshly squeezed lemonade jug under the branches of the old orange tree that had been there long before the Meletis family could remember. Although its fruit-bearing days were over, it still created a lovely shade for the family to sit under.

From the kitchen, the aroma of freshly baked biscuits reached Alexandros. Anghela had been baking again. Cooking and baking, knitting and crochet were all Anghela's hobbies, including lovingly looking after her three boys.

She would be calling the whole family now to partake in a cool drink in the garden and a piece of cake or some homemade biscuits. This was an opportunity for a family get-together and a chance for a chat about how everyone's day had fared. This was now a routine that had been established since they were newly married.

There was no hurry; the siesta had relaxed them all, even if everyone had not been able to sleep during the siesta hour, just lying relaxed away from the harsh midday sun enabled the whole family to emerge refreshed and ready to stay up well into the night.

All the beauty that surrounded Alexandros together with all the homely sounds that came from within his household had failed to lift the unhappy and restless mood he had fallen into from the moment the messenger had come bringing with him news that would shatter the whole household.

Restless now and unwilling to settle to the task at hand, he stood up and started pacing the room like a caged lion. He knew that whatever he tried to do, he was hopelessly inadequate to stop the impending course of events that would occur.

Quite simply, a man had come to inform Alexandros that the very next day, baby Ahmed's master would return and that upon his return, he would be making his way to Alexandros and his family to seek and take the child away.

As of tomorrow, the child would no longer be with them. They would no longer see him darting in and out of the house, squealing and frightening the chickens, and chasing the old dog who in view of his old age had long ago earned the right to find a hiding place and spend his remaining years quietly sleeping in the shade, instead of being chased all around by a boisterous two-year-old boy!

How was he to tell Anghela that she would no longer be putting him to sleep with a cuddle and a song, wiping the tears the many, many times he had fallen and hurt himself, or as it often happened, scold him for his boisterous antics.

He also knew that Noti too would miss his little companion that followed him around like a shadow, closely and lovingly.

Alexandros shut his eyes tight, trying to picture more clearly the events that had led to this dreaded moment.

A Debt of Honour

Sitting in the kitchen and watching Anghela remove tray after tray of biscuits from the coal-fired range while little Ahmed burnt his fingers as he tried to pinch them before they cooled down, Alexandros told her in a matter of fact voice of the father's coming the very next day to take away Ahmed from their midst.

Anghela continued to remove the biscuits that were ready, and like an automat, filled the biscuit tins. No word was spoken. It was as if she did not want to understand the meaning of her husband's monologue. Effectively, she carried on as if he had not spoken, as if the forthcoming morrow was of no importance to her other than what she was doing right now.

The silence deepened after the news about tomorrow's event was delivered. Alexandros himself was silent. Nothing stirred in the kitchen. Ahmed had run outside in the garden with a handful of freshly baked biscuits in his hands, chuckling away.

Noti, who had just finished his homework and had come down in the kitchen ready for a bite to eat, heard the news too. He stood transfixed by the door he had just entered from, and his gaze was now on his mother, trying to fathom how the news had affected her, knowing full well the pain that she would have to endure at Ahmed's departure.

The dog came running from the garden, closely followed by Ahmed, who was laughingly chasing him. As if awakening from a spell, the three of them stirred. Noti ran and put his arms around his mother and gave her a kiss on both cheeks. Alexandros took the already prepared lemonade jug and the plate of freshly baked biscuits which Anghela had laid out and, out of habit, walked into the garden where the table was ready. Silently, the adults ate. It was a routine gesture, but unlike the many late afternoons previously, today, no one spoke. Everyone was locked away in their own train of thought.

That night, Anghela and Alexandros hardly slept a wink. Many a time Anghela would silently get out of bed and go over to Ahmed's cot and lovingly look at the youngster sleeping like a cherub—innocent and sweet. Very gently, she would stroke his lovely head of black curls and then return to bed next to Alexandros.

The vigil of pain had begun. Soon after daybreak, they would have only the memoirs of the youngster they had so lovingly taken into their hearts and into their lives.

Dawn broke. The Meletis family resumed the task that every morning brought forth. Anghela prepared an omelette from the freshly laid eggs that the chickens had produced this very morning and which Noti had brought into the kitchen, as was his habit, for the family's breakfast. Only today, no one apart from Ahmed ate.

Anghela was already on her second cup of strong Greek coffee, and Alexandros, who usually preferred camomile tea when he was at home, today had drunk too many cups of the strong Greek drink. They both felt they needed something strong to give their systems a jolt, for, after last night's sleeplessness, they felt jaded and low.

Quietly now, Alexandros retraced his steps away from the kitchen and, watching Anghela resume her household tasks, returned to his study. Heavily he sat down into his chair. The paperwork on his table required his attention. He knew he could not continue to neglect the project for long, but right now, he couldn't face the task. His brain had gone into hibernation along with his whole body.

The sound of the front door knocker gave him a shudder, yet he was reluctant to move from his seat.

He heard the happy sounds of greetings at the front door. It was a friend of Noti's who had come to call for him to walk the few miles to school together. He heard the shout of "Adio Baba, Adio Mama", "Goodbye Dad, Goodbye Mum", as Noti swung the front door shut behind him and

Alexandros settled once more into his reverie. Anghela was going about busily making the beds, and from the sounds coming from the room above, she would still be making Ahmed's cot up, forestalling in her mind the moment of departure for a while at least.

There was no siesta for the family today; the waiting game had begun. No one was hungry, and no one sat at the table at lunchtime. Anghela never ventured into the kitchen to prepare something quick and delicious, as was her habit every day.

Silently the house awaited the knock on the door.

Sometime after one o'clock in the afternoon, the sound of horses' hooves was heard from the open doors of the study. The rider alighted and tied the horse to the gatepost and made his way to the front door.

Before he had time to raise the knocker, Alexandros opened the door. Anghela stood behind him, and by her side was Noti, who had now returned from school. They made an attractive frozen picture. Alexandros was the first to recover. A smile came to his face, and the hand of friendship was extended in welcome to the visitor now standing in front of him.

Taking him by the arm, Alexandros led Suliman to Anghela and Noti and introduced them. Alexandros,

Anghela and Noti spoke fluent Turkish, the language of the country they were living in, as well as Greek, their mother tongue.

After the perfunctory greetings were over, Alexandros led the boy's father, Suliman, through the kitchen into the back garden where Ahmed was busily playing in the sandpit that Alexandros had made for him.

Suliman, choking with emotion now, rushed and swung little Ahmed high above his head, and when the squeals of delight had died down, he lovingly crushed him to his chest, filling his head with kisses and openly crying at the sight of the boy so grown up now—a boy who had been a baby the last time he had seen him.

Alexandros, Anghela and Noti quietly left the father and his son together in the garden. From the kitchen window, they could see the boy showing his father the kotetsi and showing off to his dad now, ran round and round, making the chickens squawk and squawk.

After a while, Suliman and his son came into the kitchen where Anghela had laid the table full of little titbits for the traveller. She knew he had journeyed from afar and that travelling from Constantinople on horseback to Smyrna was a long and tiresome journey.

Sitting around the table now, with the boy demanding the attention of his father, Alexandros and Anghela filled him in on all the stories of little Ahmed from the time he had been brought over to them.

The father laughed at the many stories of his son's antics. He was glad that the part of his son's life missing while he was gone was now being filled with all the details that he had never known.

The boy, now having everyone's attention, started chasing the old dog around the house into the garden. The grown-ups laughed, and the youngster knew that he could do no wrong today. The more they laughed, the more mischievous he became. No one had the heart to scold him. Today was the last time Anghela, Alexandros and Noti were to see, hear and love him. For it was indeed a rule that the Turks and the Christians never visited or went to each other's house. NEVER!

The minutes were precious now; after tonight, he would no longer belong to them. He would go away, perhaps never to be seen again, and they had no say whatsoever in the matter.

Ahmed's father quietly asked if he could speak to Alexandros privately. Alexandros led him into the study, and both men sat facing each other. The young man, Alexandros now observed, was the absolute double of his son. Beautiful jet-black hair and long black lashed eyes fringed his face, a face that looked stern and strong, yet when he spoke and smiled, the corner of his lips crinkled into a lovely kind smile. Everything about this young man spoke of strength and determination, yet of kindness and openness too.

Alexandros liked him, and his first impression of him was right. He was sure that Ahmed would have a wonderful father in the young man that now sat opposite him.

Silently now, the two men smoked a cigarette each. Alexandros felt that the young man had something on his mind, something that he was reluctant to come out with and say.

Taking the initiative, Alexandros proceeded to tell him that he and his family had come to love Ahmed like one of their own and that Anghela had taken the child to her heart and would be devastated at his departure from his home for good.

He went on to assure the father that he had been well looked after, had plenty to occupy him and what was, he felt, very important to the young man now, told him that at no point during the time that Ahmed had lived with them, had the family taken him to church with them. He had respected the fact that Ahmed was a Muslim and as such entering the

Christian church was against his religion. He furthermore informed Suliman that at no time did Ahmed partake in the eating of pork, as he knew and respected the fact that the Muslim religion vigorously forbade this. The pork was from the pig, and the pig in their eyes was an unclean animal.

Suliman now stood up and, facing Alexandros, took a few steps forward and, grasping Alexandros firmly by the shoulders, thanked him profusely.

"The love you have shown to my son and the respect you have given to the religion he was born into makes me indeed grateful and deeply indebted to you and all your family", said Suliman.

Standing back, he quietly proceeded to take a pouch out of his pocket and, untying the string at the top, poured a handful of gold coins onto the desk that held all Alexandros' drawings and sketches.

Looking at Alexandros, who did not comprehend that gesture, he continued, "The love you have given to my son, I can never repay, but please accept this worthless gesture of a few gold coins, not nearly enough, yet a small gesture of my deepest gratitude to you and your family for everything you have done for my family".

Alexandros took a moment or two before replying. On the one hand, he did not want to offend the giver of the gesture of kindness. On the other hand, he knew that he, Anghela and Noti could not and would not accept any payment for something that they had done in total and absolute love.

Taking the pouch now in both his hands, he proceeded to scoop the valued gold coins back inside. Once this was done, closely watched by the young man, he tied the string tight and, holding the pouch in one hand, drew the young man's hand towards him and placed the now full pouch in the palm of Suliman's hand with a quiet shake of the head.

Suliman stood staring at Alexandros now. Slowly his eyes were clouding with washed tears. He put the pouch once again back into his shirt's pocket and quietly grasped both Alexandros' arms in his and spoke, "For your kindness and love shown to my son, and the respect portrayed to our religion, I am beholden to you and your family for the rest of my life! My family is your family from this moment on, and should you ever need or seek our help in whatever form, you shall be repaid a thousand-fold, my brother!"

Here in this very study, a bond had been forged between the Christian Greek and the Muslim Turk; a bond between two people of different faiths and different origins, who for a brief moment in time had overcome the barriers that existed in the crazy world of religions, origins and segregations.

Little did either Alexandros or Suliman dream that the fates were at this very moment formulating a blueprint on which the debt would be exchanged for the lives of those present. This was indeed a debt of honour!

A Turn of Events

The year is 1919

It was the early hours on the fifteenth day of May.

The sun shone on a cloudless, beautiful day, and the people had already thronged around Smyrna harbour in their thousands. There was a definite air of expectancy, and merrymaking was in full swing when Alexandros reached the periphery of the harbour.

What had brought Alexandros there was not a desire to partake in the happy festivity that was taking place all around him now, by his fellow Greeks, who were so obviously enjoying themselves, but seeing for himself the turn of events he dreaded. Many Greeks thought today was the day to celebrate the freedom that President Venizelos had envisioned.

It was said that a Greek army had been gathering in Greece and was preparing to march into Smyrna to release the Greek people from the Turks.

Alexandros and his family, together with a very small minority of Greeks, had not rushed to the harbour that day. Instead of rejoicing, they held silent and fearful thoughts in the very depth of their hearts.

How many times Alexandros had loudly voiced his opinion that "a ripple had been started that could lead to the churning of a huge tidal wave". He held a premonition that President Venizelos had stirred a hornets' nest that would obliterate and cause chaos and destruction all around, on a scale never before seen.

That was the reason why today of all days Anghela and Noti had decided to stay at home, each with their thoughts, heavy with apprehension at what could follow, and sadly feeling no joy, only dreadful unrest.

Greek battleships and troopships had now moved slowly, silently and stealthily into the harbour as dawn in all its beauty came up.

The whole Greek population, it seemed to Alexandros, had turned out to greet the Greek army, most in their national Greek costumes, which they had donned in their honour.

The unforgettable sunny day turned into a festive merrymaking occasion with outbursts of singing and dancing in and around the harbour. Stalls were quickly set up, lambs slaughtered and roasted on-site. And as Greeks love any opportunity of a festivity, everyone had come to toast the end of years of enslavement.

Everyone in the crowd was in a happy holiday mood. Shops were shut, vineyards silent and the fields deserted, as they came in their thousands to cheer, together with the Armenian population and the Jews, who had also come to welcome the liberators.

Monsignor Chrysostomos, the then much beloved and popular Greek Metropolitan Patriarch of Smyrna turned out resplendent in his richly embroidered robes of gold and blue, thus giving the seal of approval of the Greek Orthodox Church by openly holding an open-air liturgy and blessing of the Greek troops that were arriving.

Alas, that gesture was to later cost him his life in those dark and dismal times that were to follow.

Alexandros had by now seen enough—he did not wish to linger any longer nor partake in any of the fun that everyone around him seemed to be having. With a heavy heart, he now retraced his steps towards home and his family. They would be waiting for news of the arrival of the Greek troops.

What was the real reason for the presence of the Greek troopships on this fine day of May in Smyrna harbour?

What were the Greeks, Armenians and Jews celebrating with such fervour?

There was now a feeling of general unrest and apprehension; an unspoken fear mingled with sadness. A knowledge that everyone kept close to their hearts, that the succeeding events could shatter the very core of their everyday complacent existence. Like a huge tidal wave that everyone expects, but no one knows for sure what far-reaching effect it will have on all of them, fear and uncertainty were now part of their thoughts.

Their destiny was about to be decided upon, fought over, and they, the Smyrniots, were powerless to do anything or have a say in the matter.

Many candles were lit in churches, and an extraordinary number of people attended Greek mass. The pews were overflowing, many prayers were sent to heaven, and women crossed themselves over and over again. They never imagined that the events to follow would be talked about throughout history.

The Tide Turns Round to the Turks

The year is 1922

On 9th September, a General called Mustafa arose and came from Salonica, Greece, and proceeded to turn the tide of utter despair, restoring Turkish Nationalism once more. He acquired the name of Kemal, meaning 'Perfection' and Atatürk, meaning 'Father of the Turks'.

With Kemal Atatürk leading them, the Nationalistic Turkish Army gathered in their tens of thousands seeking revenge. They were so inflamed to a fever pitch, thoroughly rested and equipped that the attack took the Greeks unaware, allowing them to annihilate five Greek divisions and capture thousands of prisoners.

The Turks had broken through the Greek lines. The defeated Greek army, now tired and wounded, had no option but to make their way slowly towards Smyrna.

It was said that the Turks now cheered and clapped and that Kamal Atatürk, very much like Nero did all those years ago, said, "Turkey is purged of the traitors and foreigners, and Turkey is for the Turks now!" The day the Greeks celebrated when the troopships arrived at Smyrna harbour was a stark contrast to the reality that followed.

Those that had tried to escape by going to church lost their lives when they were torched along with the people inside. It was rumoured that Aristotle Onassis—a big entrepreneur, also born in Karatas—bribed his way out and escaped. He, like Noti, was from the same village.

Alexandros, Anghela and Noti heard that Monsignor Chrysostomos was summoned by the Turkish Commander of the Barracks. He was warned that his life was in danger, but a French patrol of twenty men said they could take him to the French Consulate-General or the Sacre-Coeur for safety. But Chrysostomos declined, saying that he was a shepherd, and therefore, must remain with his flock.

There followed a derisory interrogation with Chrysostomos, the outcome of which was in the light of events that followed, an exact repetition of the sentence that Pontius Pilate had passed on to Christ all those many, many years ago.

For now, too, the Turkish Commander, turning to the mob which had gathered waiting beneath his balcony, proclaimed, "Treat him as he deserves".

Like Christ, Chrysostomos was then released into the care of the crowd, who then proceeded to beat him with their hands, fists and sticks. They spat on his face, riddled him with stabs, tore his beard off, gouged his eyes out and cut his nose and ears off.

The French patrol accompanied the Patriarch as a gesture but was under the strictest order not to interfere. They watched the massacre scene, trembling with indignation, in a state of pure agitation at what they had witnessed. Despite their want to intervene, their officer forbade them to move. They were held by gunpoint!

Justice had been done. They had repaid Chrysostomos for the offence of blessing the Greek troops when they took over the city three years ago.

That was the sum total of his crimes.

The murder of the Patriarch was soon perceived as a license to murder and loot.

Every Armenian and Greek in Smyrna had become a refugee from terror, and this included the Jews as well.

Slowly as the sun rose now on this fateful and unforgettable day of Saturday, the 4th Turkish Cavalry Regiment enclosed Smyrna, acting as an advance guard for the Turkish Nationalist Army, who were led by Mustafa Kemal Atatürk.

Silently and steadfastly, this troop of fierce and bellicose soldiers entered Smyrna now. Riding on horseback, they struck fear and sheer terror to everyone that stood in their path. They then proceeded to loot, rape and kill whole families, throwing their bodies into the streets like some discarded rubbish.

This was no battle. It was a massacre, pure and simple— the systematic butchering of peaceful, unarmed villagers by a horde of ruthless, blood-thirsty soldiers. When the sun set that evening, dead bodies flooded the streets, many decapitated and separated from other body parts—evidence of what the war had become.

Escape to Safety

Alexandros, Anghela and Noti sat in pitch-black darkness in their home, afraid to show any sign of light. Trembling and cowering with fear, they listened with trepidation at every sound they heard. All day long, they heard the Turkish soldiers thundering past on horseback, their destination being Smyrna harbour.

By nightfall, both Alexandros and Anghela had resigned themselves to the fact that should they choose to remain, a sure and certain death warrant lay waiting for them, despite the fact that their house lay well hidden from the road and a ways from the harbour.

But like the sand in an egg timer, their time was up. In order to try and reach safety, they had to attempt to escape. But the question was—where? After one last look at the house they had lived all their lives in, and making sure that the gold sovereigns they had saved all those years painstakingly lay safely sewn in the hem of Anghela's dress, they set off, trudging wearily and silently toward the only route they felt they could take—the harbour.

After what seemed like an eternity, they finally reached their destination. But upon reaching there, they encountered mayhem. The Turkish soldiers were riding on horseback through the crowd, clutching in their hands scimitars and systemically decapitating anyone who crossed their path. The foul stench of blood mingled with death all around them, filled their senses, but despair drove Alexandros on. Meanwhile, death lingered on, and hung like mist in the air.

Weary, desperate, and with no shred of hope in her heart, Anghela continued to follow Alexandros, not even attempting to find out where he was leading them to. Every few steps, she stopped to embrace Noti and hug him closer. There were no miracles left, no plea bargaining with God, no votive offerings, no prayers that her trembling lips could utter. She felt that their God had all but abandoned each and every one of them.

Reaching the periphery of the harbour and standing as close to the wall behind them as possible, Alexandros suddenly saw in front of him a woman trying to hide from the horseman, who quickly struck her down in one fell swoop. Alas, in front of their eyes, they recognised their neighbour Fotini, the kind woman who had helped so many people, sitting night after night holding the hand of someone whose life was slowly ebbing away, who had helped deliver babies, and who had baked and cooked for those who couldn't look after themselves. In Greek tradition, the dying would never be left alone, with neighbours rallying around, taking turns to sit and care for them until they took their last breath.

"Let's go!" Alexandros shouted, gripping Anghela's arm.

"All right, but where?"

"Anywhere! As long as it is far away from here…" Alexandros replied. An idea born out of sheer desperation crossed Alexandros' mind. All three were now playing hide and seek with death, in the Devil's own grotesque playground, amidst the chaos of God's own forgotten humanity.

Demoralised and forlorn, Anghela only hoped that death, which she felt inevitable, would be swift for all three of them and that they would all be together when that final moment came.

Noti, now overwhelmed and exhausted with fear and sheer tiredness, stopped and would not take another step. Anghela wiped the tears that were threatening to engulf her whole being and yanked Noti, pushing him in front of her as if by that gesture, she would erase the harrowing scenes that all three had witnessed so far.

"I'm frightened manoula mou (mama)", whimpered Noti. "I'm sorry agapi mou (my love)", she whispered. "I didn't mean to take it out on you. Of course, you're frightened. We all are. What you must remember is that everything looks and feels different and worse than it is. We're together now. Together we are invincible. I want you to always remember that".

Freedom or Death?

Alexandros, Anghela and Noti walked, stumbled, crawled and hid throughout the night, with Alexandros silently leading the way. His shoulders were hunched, his clothes torn and tattered, but his head held high. His footsteps followed his thoughts while he stopped every now and then to let Anghela and Noti catch up with him.

Little did his family know that he was playing his last bid for freedom in a gamble that could easily lead to instant death for all three of them. For if his dangerous act failed, Haros, the Death Collector, would have an ultimate say in the matter.

They had now walked all night. Weary and frightened, they saw the break of dawn. Ironically, a beautiful orange blast of colour filled the sky, creating a sight so beautiful that it made all three of them stop and think that this was indeed a wonderful world, and surely if God's hand had painted such wondrous dawn, it was an omen that death had no dark part to play in it. Death could no longer be lurking around on such a beautiful day!

Finally, they came to what seemed like a large estate, a farm of sorts, and as they approached the veranda of the house, with many acres of land around it, Alexandros doggedly increased his pace and, turning to Anghela, silently beckoned her to follow him.

But Anghela had stopped, frozen with fear. She had recognised it as a working Turkish farm. The sound of hens clucking, the cockerel crowing and the chorus of birds singing confirmed her worst fears. Alexandros, it seemed in her befuddled mind, had every intention of surrendering them into the hands of the Turks who owned that farm!

Like a broken and thrown away rag doll, Anghela collapsed on the hard ground surrounding the steps to the veranda, but Alexandros, with a determined shrug, climbed the steps to the front of the house. With just a moment's hesitation, he got hold of the door knocker and, with a resolute hand, loudly knocked twice.

After a few moments that seemed like ages, the door was opened by a farmworker. He was a lad of around sixteen, who, after making eye contact with Alexandros, let his eyes wander to where Anghela was now trying to sit up with the help of Noti.

Recovering from his surprise at finding on the doorstep three Greeks who had boldly knocked at his master's house, he started shrieking, "eeeeee, eeeee!"

As if from nowhere, they were immediately surrounded by a houseful of people. A big fat lady who looked like a cook, with an apron tied around her waist, came out of the kitchen, followed by two servants with long white robes. They all gathered around the three intruders.

Hearing the great commotion and shrieks, the master who was working in his study quickly stood up and, opening a drawer, withdrew a hand pistol. Swiftly and silently, he emerged into the hallway, where his staff and servants had surrounded a man, a woman and a boy.

Silently, he seized the gist of the situation, and with his eyes like burning braziers, stood in front of Alexandros with utter contempt. For it seemed to him that the three Christians had the audacity to seek asylum in his home—in the house of a Turk!

Alexandros had not just taken his family to any old farmhouse; this was, in fact, the property of a man he once met, who many years ago had entrusted his family with his one and only son. This was Suliman's house.

Those few steps from the entrance hall to Suliman's study seemed to Alexandros like following the executioner, for indeed, he was the executor of their fate. He proceeded to stare at Alexandros with eyes full of hatred and waited for an explanation. Proudly and with his head held high, Alexandros challenged Suliman. He did not bow, cry or seek help; he was not going to procrastinate. He knew instinctively that it would be to no avail. He was a Greek, and in times such as these, the enemy.

Did Suliman recognise Alexandros? Did he remember him from all of those years back, when hands were shook, and a debt of honour was exchanged?

Anghela and Noti stood frozen to the spot, unable to take their eyes off the two protagonists, knowing in their bones that this was a drama unfolding. The two men were the players in a game of chess, and their lives were the pawns.

Inexorably now, Alexandros, with more bravado than he was actually feeling, stood before Suliman and reminded him of his pledge when he had come to collect his son many years ago. Alexandros had wanted no payment at the time, and just as he collected Ahmed, Suliman had vowed:

"For all the kindness and love shown to my son, and the respect portrayed to my religion during his stay with your family, I am beholden to you and your family, for should you ever need or seek help in whatever form, you shall be repaid a thousand-fold, my brother".

Suliman now closed his eyes. No sound was heard, except for the slow ticking of a clock somewhere in the house. They were all frozen like discarded puppets. Slowly now, after what seemed like an eternity to Alexandros, Suliman raised his head and, looking at Alexandros, took a key out of a small box that was sitting on his desk, and opening a drawer, took a pouch with some gold sovereigns. He then pushed it towards Alexandros, shrugging his shoulders. He had contracted his obligation, and that was his method of repayment.

Like a scene from the past, a silent movie being played in a dark recess of his brain, Alexandros, for the second time in his life, shook his head, and looking straight at Suliman, pushed the pouch back towards its owner.

Puzzled now, Suliman spread his hands in a gesture of pure perplexity and, speaking in a hushed tone, asked, "What now?" whereupon Alexandros informed him that whilst they had no need for his material help, he sought to escape together with his family, away from Smyrna! It didn't matter where, just away from the holocaust that was all around them.

This new request seemed to have taken Suliman by surprise. Once more, he closed his eyes and proceeded to silently lose himself in his thoughts.

Alexandros and his family did not dare breathe. The moment had come when they would either live or die, and the man sitting in front of them held their lives in the palm of his hand.

After a few moments of meditation, Suliman looked up, and after careful consideration, delivered his verdict.

"I have fought with my conscience. It was not an easy battle. Whatever step I took, I am bound to be a loser, one way or another. But my honour as a man, and the love of my son, is greater than the love of my country at the moment. You have won! I shall be sending you with one of my most trusted servants in a caique. But from this moment on, my debt to you has been repaid. The sacrifice is enormous and know if we perchance ever happen to meet again, it will be as enemies! GO NOW! And I hope never to set eyes upon you all ever again!"

Suliman had repaid the debt of all those years ago and wiped out the old score. Honour had been absolved. The kindness of Alexandros and Anghela towards Suliman all those years ago had been returned. Suliman gave the family their last lifeline amidst the war that would have otherwise cost them their lives. Reprieved, Alexandros knew how burdensome Suliman's gesture must have been to him, and whilst waiting for the instructions that were to follow, turned around to his family, embraced them all tightly, knowing they had walked through the nightmare into a land of living and hope once more. A new life beckoned them on.

They had made it! Haros was no longer on their heels. They were the lucky ones; their faith in God was restored once more. They would live to tell the tale to their grandchildren, and what a tale it would be!

Little did they know that if they had remained in Smyrna any longer, their fate would have been very different. On 13th September 1922, Turkish soldiers set fire to the city of Smyrna, burning most of the Greek and Armenian quarters, forcing thousands of refugees to the ports waterfront, desperate to escape. Families were faced with only three options: to risk drowning in the sea, to be burnt alive by the flames or to be executed by the Turkish soldiers. The Great Fire of Smyrna lasted nine days, until it was mostly extinguished on 22nd September. Thousands of Greeks and Armenians lost their lives to the fire which caused mass destruction to a complete city, entirely eradicating Orthodox Christianity in Smyrna. The Muslim and Jewish quarters escaped damage. To this day, the exact death toll number is not known. The Greco-Turkish War (1919-1922) and the Great Fire of Smyrna (1922) continue to be two of the darkest moments in Greek history.

The War is Over

After being dropped at the island of Lesvos by Suliman's faithful and jaundice-eyed servant, and with the help of the golden sovereigns sewn in the hem of Anghela's skirt, Alexandros, Anghela and Noti made their way to Greece. There, they found they were looked upon as a subculture. They found Greece desolate, with no prospects of either jobs or help. So, they left Greece and made their way to Alexandria to seek their fortune and a new life.

The world was made aware of the enormous burden now shouldered by Greece and the Red Cross, together with other charities from America, came over seeking to give help. In the meantime, typhus and dysentery were also prevalent. For eight months, the Red Cross fed and helped an average of 600,000 refugees per month, whilst the Greek government coped as well as it could with the rest. They built huts and houses for the rising population, and today, nostalgic names such as 'Nea Smyrnia' can still be found, reminiscence of the settlements at the time. The 'Rembetes' (musical storytellers) from Smyrna would often sit in cafes drinking cup after cup of strong Greek coffee, playing with their worry beads and composing songs in a mournful rhyme. The words were all about the sorrow of their plight, the difficulty of finding jobs and all the while remembering their lost home and land in Turkey.

Having fed and looked after thousands of refugees, alas, the money ran out. The Red Cross stayed in Greece from 15th November 1922 to 30th June 1923, leaving enough supplies for a further six weeks. After no longer having sufficient assets, they had to withdraw. President Venizelos was understandably ousted from power, and his downfall brought about the abdication of King Constantinos of Greece who was succeeded by George II to rule over a country that was virtually bankrupt!

The last stitches of the tapestry of life for the Greeks in Smyrna had been brought to an abrupt close with the final stitches not in silver and gold, but in blood red and blackened with the flames of fire.

Noti and his family had witnessed unbelievable atrocities whilst making their escape.

This then was the background of Panayotis Meletis, the memory of which would never fade—a legacy that he could carry with him throughout his life.

From the ashes of Smyrna rose modern Izmir, the third-largest city of Turkey and its busiest port. The years went by, and the final act of inhumanity and degradation was matted by the then Ruler Mohamed, who had conquered

Constantinople, and proceeded to seize The Holy Byzantine Church of Saint Sophia that was built fourteen hundred years before by Emperor Justinian I, who then boasted that he had excelled Solomon and his temple.

The Church of Saint Sophia, which was turned into a mosque.

The much-loved Greek Orthodox Church of Saint Sophia was henceforth turned into a mosque and used for the Muslims. It was stripped of its finery and its frescoes plastered over. With four new minarets, one at each corner of the building, it became the most splendid mosque the Mohamedan religion possessed.

This final act of profanity, degradation and desecration was felt deeply by all Greeks. Many years later, books were printed by those who had escaped. Memories were dredged;

everyone felt and shared once again those dark days of long ago.

The Greco-Turkish War was a war that had been fought a long, long time ago and now belonged in the yellowed and forgotten pages of the history books. But this history is not forgotten by those survivors of the human catastrophe who were lucky enough to have fled the holocaust. For them, the memory still lingers in their minds and through the countless tales told by their grandchildren.

Eyewitnesses were brought forth to tell the tale of the war that had been fought many years ago and the price paid in both pain and blood, which had left the rest of the world with a feeling of shame for belonging to the human race.

Long after the ink had dried on the yellowed pages of the history books, and the earth had soaked the blood of those raped, killed and burnt to death, the offspring and the grandchildren of those who had endured and managed to escape, recount, reveal and embroider the terrible tale of Smyrna.

Who ultimately knows what truth is and what is a figment of the imagination or a stretch of exaggeration of those long gone by days?

Only those who were there knew, and most of them no longer roam the realms of this world. But through their memories lives the long-forgotten tales of Smyrna—that proud and treasured city that Alexander the Great had dreamt of and had so lovingly built.

Hopefully, the barriers that exist in today's crazy world of religions, origins, segregations and cults will one day collapse and the world will unite in an ideology of good and helping each other will be the only right way forward.

In the land of hope, there is no winter.

Lightning Source UK Ltd.
Milton Keynes UK
UKHW020953291122
412996UK00012B/351